HOW ANIMALS COMMUNICATE

HOW ANIMALS COMMUNICATE

Jan Zdarek
Edited by Inga Smith

HAMLYN

Picture acknowledgements (numbers denote the number of photographs)

Bartoš, L.: 79, Chvapil, S.: 1, Chvojka, M.: 5, Diviš, T.: 2, Dvořák, K.: 2,
Eberhardt, G., W.: 1, Haragsim, O.: 1, Hauser, L.: 12, Heráň, I.: 2, Horák, J.: 1, Kaftan, M.: 8,
Křeček, J.: 11, Kučera, J.: 1, Macháček, P.: 6, Pokora, D.: 3, Rödl, P.: 4, Studnička, E.: 8,
Ševčík, Jan: 16, Ševčík Josef: 1, Šmíd, J.: 1, Vávra, J.: 1, Velísek, V.: 1, Vít, Z.: 5, Zumr, J.: 10,
Žďárek, J.: 28.

Line drawings by M. Váňa
Published by The Hamlyn Publishing Group Limited,
a Division of The Octopus Publishing Group plc
Michelin House, 81 Fulham Road
London SW3 6RB, England
and distributed for them by
Octopus Distribution Services Limited
Rushden, Northants, England
Copyright © 1988 Artia, Prague
This English language edition first published 1988

ISBN 0 600 55037 0
Printed in Czechoslovakia by TSNP Martin
3/20/01/51-01

DEFENDING ONE'S RESOURCES

LOOKING FOR A MATE

MATING

TAKING CARE OF THE BROOD

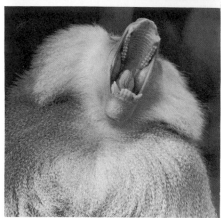

ESTABLISHING SOCIAL POSITION

LOOKING FOR FOOD

AVOIDING PREDATION

Every nation has tales in which a few humans are privileged to converse with animals. Modern science begins to change this fantasy into reality, and the privileged ones are ethologists. There are, of course, no easy, fairy tale style methods for mastering the tongues of our fellow earth creatures. The understanding is often acquired only after countless hours of painstaking observations of Nature and by endless studies of animal behaviour in laboratories. The privileged place of man among living creatures has dulled our senses and deprived us of the ability to be aware of the multitude of messages sent throughout the wilderness, let alone to understand them. Hence, beyond the limits of our sensations, sophisticated instruments become inter-mediaries, through which we challenge the canniness of Nature with the cunning of the human brain. This book aims to be a testimony to the triumphant endeavours as well as the frustrations of enquiring people; people who equip themselves for an expedition into the realms of understanding the mysterious relationships among living creatures, into the worlds of animal language.

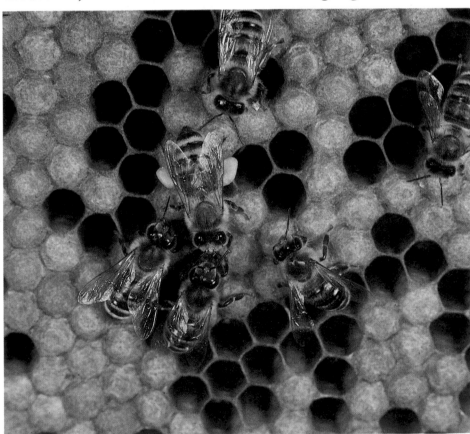

DEFENDING ONE'S RESOURCES

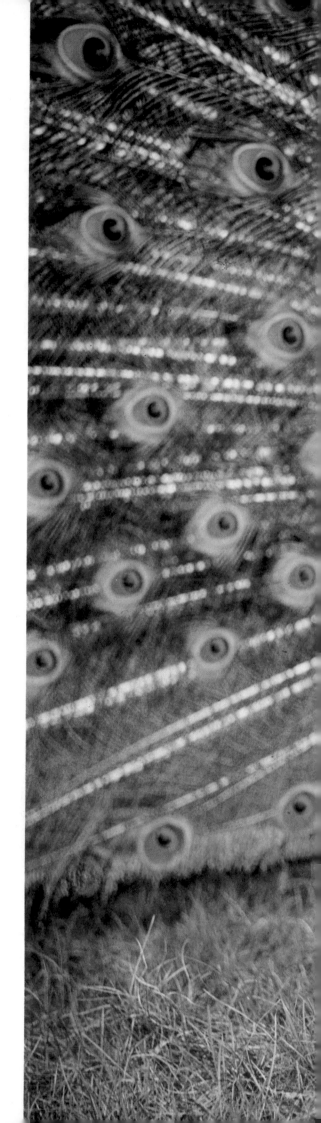

The notion of freedom and liberty is often epitomized by saying 'free as a bird'. The comparison is, however, utterly false. The idea that a bird is free to go anywhere it chooses was disproved over a hundred years ago by the German zoologist Bernhard Altum. He was the first to formulate the opinion that birds divide among themselves the available environment (biotope) into individual territories. Each territory has well-defined boundaries, and the owner defends it against intruders of its own species. Thus the concept of territoriality was established which later proved to be an almost universal principle for the co-existence of all animals including birds, mammals, reptiles, amphibians and many invertebrates. Elements of territorial behaviour can certainly be seen in humans.

Considering the infinite variety of forms and behaviours in animals, it was not easy for scientists to find a universally valid definition of territoriality which would fit all the ways of dividing a living space among animals. It is generally accepted that territoriality exists whenever an animal defends resources against other individuals, whether of its own or another species. The hitch in this definition is that it may not always be clearly determined what constitutes a resource and just what is to be considered a defence. An animal can defend almost anything: a source of food, a suitable place for reproduction, a strategic position for defence against predators. Animals defend their 'property' in countless ways.

8

Territorial behaviour is easy to spot wherever there is overt aggressiveness against intruders. We can find obvious examples among many birds. The most violent encounters can be seen in early spring, when nesting territories are being established. Those boisterous contests among robins or finches are not, as people often think, fights over females. A closer look will reveal that females are often in the fray themselves. The catalyst for fighting is a trespasser on one's territory. Since the one in possession of the area is more confident of his position and more strongly motivated, he usually wins the encounter. The defender's aggression is strongest in the middle of his territory and decreases toward the periphery. A territory can be compared to a rubber ball: the more you squeeze it, the less it gives to your pressure. On territorial boundaries the tendency to attack is replaced by an inclination to flee. It is in this zone that most disputes are waged. Animals armed with dangerous weapons such as sharp teeth or claws generally do not use them for territorial disputes. If a simple threat is not enough to repel an intruder, a ritualized fight takes place. The opponents compare their strength by making harmless gestures, postures or other signals according to the 'rules of the game'. A long, bloody fight is quite an exception, since the weaker contestant yields before he gets seriously injured. Evolution has favoured individuals that can quickly recognize their defeat. 'He who fights and runs away, lives to fight another day.'

More often animals maintain their exclusive areas by less spectacular means. Neighbours may not even meet, yet they respect boundaries between each other. Often the only clue one has that an area is divided into territories is that the inhabitants are spaced out more regularly than would happen by chance.

Even though marking, patrolling and defending a territory uses up a lot of energy, territoriality is common among animals of all evolutionary stages. What advantage, then, does ownership of a territory bring?

First, it secures an even exploitation of a suitable biotope by the given species. Each individual occupies an area just big enough to provide itself with the necessary resources for survival and reproduction. That is why the size of the territories varies greatly according to the size of the animal and its feeding habits. Herbivores regularly inhabit areas considerably smaller than those of the carnivores that prey on them. The size of territories also depends on the richness of resources in the landscape. For instance, hares have much smaller boundaries in the fertile lowlands than they do in the poorer, hilly country. Territories of small animals such as mice, fish, lizards or frogs may consist of only a few square metres, and the range of insects is even smaller. Conversely, large cats or birds of prey have territories that are described in square kilometres.

Another function of the territory is that it often serves as a meeting place for the sexes. Migratory birds are well known for using their domain for this purpose, most notably the storks. In the spring, the birds always return to their old nesting sites. It may surprise you that bird couples are more faithful to the location of their nest than they are to each other.

A well-defined domain also provides privacy to the nesting pair during courtship and while raising a family. For the female of certain species, the size and quality of a male's territory may be what she uses to judge the qualities of the future father of her offspring. A male capable of defending a rich territory is naturally preferred over the owner of an inferior property. The able owner of a good site is reproductively more successful. In the extreme case this may lead to occasional polygamy; if there is much disparity between the quality of two males' territories, the female may find it advantageous to mate with the already engaged but richer male rather than become involved with a bachelor who has meagre holdings.

When listing the advantages of territoriality, the defence function must be

Size of the territory of a buzzard, warbler, hamster and cricket.

included. Being familiar with one's own territory makes defence or escape easier, aids the self-confidence of the animal and eliminates the stress of a strange environment. The territory is a kind of selected kennel run, from which the animal can be expelled only by force. An animal deprived of its territory behaves tentatively and with much caution, constantly poised for evasion or flight. Birds without a territory have a significantly higher mortality rate than those with a property.

A fact to be noted is that not all the area in which the animal moves to hunt or to find a mate necessarily belongs to its own territory. If the area the animal has at its disposal is too large to be defended, then it is called a home range. Outside the animal's exclusive territory, which may represent only a small part of the home range, is a neutral zone. There, animals tolerate each other. For example, in seagull colonies the nesting territories of individual pairs hardly extend beyond the encompassing reach of a bird's beak when it is sitting on the nest. The home range of the colony, however, involves vast areas of the surrounding sea.

The owner of the greatest home range on land may be the Siberian tiger (*Panthera tigris altaica*). Considering this animal can cover 60 kilometres in one night, one could believe a report that the land regularly exploited by this tiger had an area of 10,000 square kilometres, which represents a square with a side of 100 kilometres! The territory, therefore, contains just enough food to satisfy the owner's requirements and no more, because a larger territory would involve greater defence costs for little extra benefit.

Results of the field studies of territorial behaviour of pied wagtails in Britain provide a good example. Wagtails defend feeding territories along river banks even in winter. In order to obtain enough food during short days at this time of the year they have to spend most of their time searching for food along the river edge and collecting insects which were washed up onto the bank. Each wagtail defends a territory of about the same length of river, and exploits it systematically by walking up one bank to the upper territory boundary, crossing the river, and then walking back down the other side until it completes the round. The length of the territory is just sufficient to enable the bird to spend time walking round the territory so that when it gets back to the starting point again the food supply will be renewed to a profitable level by washing up enough insects onto the bank. The

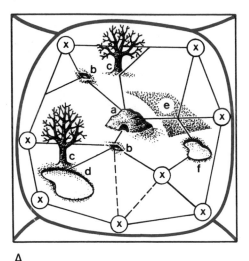 

A diagram of a hypothetical mammalian territory (A). The area defended by the animal is delineated by scent marks (x) and contains the den (a) in the middle and a network of pathways (b) along which the animal deposits its faeces. The paths connect places where the animal grazes (e), bathes (d), drinks (f) and also lead to the trees used for rubbing (c). The territory of a male damselfly (B) must contain a suitable place (marked with dots) where the female can deposit her eggs after copulations.

A   B

renewal rate of food influences not only size of the territory, but also defence behaviour of the owner. When the renewal rate is very high then the owner allows other wagtails to trespass unmolested, since it does not benefit the owner to waste time evicting intruders. At intermediate levels of food abundance the owner may defend his territory either alone, or he may allow another bird, usually a juvenile, to feed on his territory. The 'guest' bird imposes a cost by depleting the food supply, but also brings a benefit by helping the owner to defend their common domain. When food supplies decrease, the dominant bird evicts the satellite wagtail. If the renewal rate of food is very low, the owner abandons his unprofitable territory and flies off to feed elsewhere.

Now that we know roughly what territory is, and what purpose it serves, we can pursue the most interesting aspects of territorial behaviour. How do animals mark out the areas they will defend, and what measures do they use to advertize their claim and their presence within it? Instead of fences and blazoned warnings, they use the signs and signals best suited to the life style and sensory abilities of the species in question. The most conspicuous, and therefore best understood by man, are the acoustic signals; that is why they were recognized first. Acoustic signals provide infinite numbers of possibilities for individual recognition of neighbours, and for the evolution of 'local dialects'. They are easily broadcast despite the obstacles of terrain and poor visibility. Optical signals have another advantage in

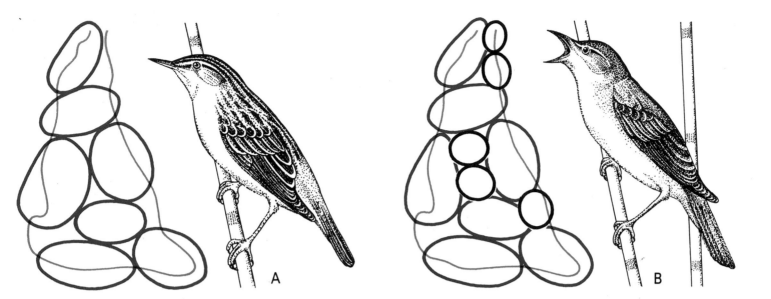

The European sedge warbler (*Acrocephalus schoenobaenus*) (B) returns in spring to the nest area later than the reed warbler (*A. scirpaceus*) (A) and consequently, it has to squeeze its own territory (marked blue) in between the territories of its relative species (marked red), the two species thus exhibiting an interspecific territorialism.

being easily localized. However, their effectiveness is restricted to rather short distances and to daylight if the signalling individual does not possess a lantern. In contrast, scent marks are used mainly by nocturnal animals or those living a secluded style of life. These marks are effective even in the absence of their owner and last longer than other kinds of signals. Electrical signalling is certainly an extravagance in the animal kingdom. It is part of the territorial behaviour of the African tapir fish (Mormyridae). The ancient Egyptians knew them and considered them to be sacred. In the muddy waters, where the tapir fish live, such wireless communication is most appreciated.

All territorial signals must possess one important property, irrespective of the sensory mode they exploit: they have to be able to convey information concerning the quality and abilities of the territory holder. Ethologists call it the resource holding power. The pitch or intensity of the voice, the complexity of acoustic signalling, the physical properties revealed in a visual display, and the size or positioning of faeces, urine or other scent marks may all convey useful information to a would-be intruder about the attributes of the resident. These will help him assess the chances for victory before the fight ever takes place.

With only a few exceptions, the territorial warning signals are meant for members of one's own species and quite often only for one's own sex. Sometimes, however, two or more species live in the same biotope and have similar ecological requirements, causing them to vie for the same food. In that case it appears advantageous for both of them to understand and respect the territorial signals of the other species. Examples of such interspecific territoriality can be found among woodpeckers, nectar birds, hummingbirds, shrikes, wheatears and crows. As one would expect, such competitors have similar appearance, vocalizations and other manifestations of their territorial behaviour.

When I was young, we country boys entertained ourselves by blowing into our cupped palms through an opening between our thumbs, thus producing the familiar sound of the cuckoo whenever that bird made itself heard in the vicinity. The cuckoo is normally a shy bird, but our noises drew it out of hiding long enough to get a look at us and excitedly respond with its own calls. This is a simple trick that everyone can do to demonstrate the involvement of vocal signals in the defence of a bird's territory. It also reliably works on the bullfinch, turtle-dove and many other birds, providing their calls are imitated accurately. The fooled male will treat the impersonators as intruders of his own species and rush to expel them from his territory with a warning. The midnight serenade of the nightingale is commonly thought to be sung for his mate, who is sweetly sleeping on the nest. It is in fact another vocal challenge. The words of his song mean 'this land is mine'. It is intended to intimidate any neighbours who might consider trespassing. The playback of a tape recording of the nightingale's song will be equally successful in defending that piece of real estate.

It is well known that not all birds sing. Many communicate by simple calls which usually provide basic information about danger and food or have a function during mating. Some birds have developed the more elaborate vocalizations that we call songs, and these carollers are the true songbirds. Approximately half of all bird species belong to this group. This by itself is a good indication of their evolutionary advantage. The factors behind their success are plain. It is what distinguishes them from their vocally less talented relatives: their ability to use not only species-specific vocalizations but also local and individual variations.

The most significant result of modern ornithological research may be the finding that a songbird does not have innate knowledge of its song but must learn it as part of its maturation. It is this very ability to acquire the song of its species with all the variations and local flourishes that eases the bird's adaptation into a new habitat and its environmental setting.

Songbirds follow general rules in learning to sing, from which individual species may differ in details. Usually only males sing, and each given species has a unique song. They learn it by listening to their fathers and other males of their kind during a short period of their early youth. In the North American white-crowned sparrow (*Zonotrichia leucophrys*), the sensitive period lasts from the tenth to the fiftieth day of its life. If the bird is deafened or shut in a sound-proof cage and thus prevented from listening to other birds, he will never learn to sing properly. During this crucial

HOW TO FOOL A CUCKOO

Acoustic signals

 chiffchaff
English

 Zilpzalp
German

 Tjiftjaf
Dutch

 czilp-czalp
Hungarian

 čipčavý kolibárik
Slovak

 Tiltaitti
Finnish

The common name of this abundant European bird, the chiffchaff (*Phylloscopus collybita*), sounds similar in many languages thanks to the unique song of the species. An analysis of the song made by the sound spectrograph is shown as recorded on a sonogram.

Storks (*Ciconia alba*) conpensate for the lack of vocal abilities by loudly clacking their beaks.

The songbirds' song-box, the syrinx, is provided with seven pairs of vocal cords, unlike other birds, which have only two pairs. These vocal cords have a more active role than human vocal cords in the production of sound. Our larynx produces a monotonous sound, which is transformed into articulated speech by the action of the larynx and mouth cavity. The syrinx of songbirds not only produces the sound but also determines the melody and rhythm — the qualities that make it a song.

period, the young bird listens only to his teacher and memorizes his song down to the finest details. He will not try out his knowledge until the following spring, at least six months after his voice lessons have ended.

There is one snag in this musical theory: how does the male nestling know, in the midst of nature's symphony of sounds, which part is meant for him? The young bird is born with a template of his species' song in his brain, and he compares it to all the sounds he hears. The template contains information about specific syllables, and the fledgling memorizes only those syllables that fit the model. When he tries his opening notes the following spring, it is as an exercise which he gradually perfects through listening to and competing with his territorial neighbours. This principle is well known to canary breeders, who give their young feathered musicians special lessons at the beginning of their careers as competition singers. In these 'schools', an older and experienced maestro sings his song to the pupils, and they try to imitate him.

Birdkeepers and birdwatchers also know that there are 'good' and 'poor' singers within each species. Variations in bird songs are what ornithologists term repertoires; in some species the repertoires number less than a hundred. In others, several thousand have been distinguished. They develop in the process of learning and probably influence a male's ability to occupy and defend his own territory. The more repertoires the singer has mastered, the greater his command over his neighbours in the challenge for territory. An able singer's best weapon is indeed in his throat. With it he can defend a larger territory, and his 'wealth' will help him attract the favour of a female.

The variability of individual songs allows the birds to identify easily their territorial neighbours. This reduces the frequency of clashes and enables a prompt recognition of strangers. Newcomers are more dangerous for a territory owner than his established neighbours, with whom boundary disputes have already been settled.

Another finding of field ornithologists, supported by sonographic recordings, is that certain bird species can produce quite different songs in different geographical regions. Their repertoires show regional similarities and can therefore be called dialects. These local songs are handed down from one generation to the next through imitation of the elders and neighbours. As in the case of human dialects before the age of radio and TV, there is a tendency to intensify the patois where populations are geographically or ecologically isolated. This may be one of the ways in which a new species arises.

Some birds have no inherited template and so can pick up the song of another species during their development. The Eurasian bullfinch (*Pyrrhula pyrrhula*) serves as a good example. If the male is incubated and brought up in a canary's nest, he will learn the song of his foster parents and, as an adult, will even ignore the song of other bullfinches. He will teach the acquired canary song to his offspring, even if he is released back into nature.

Other birds, including mocking birds (Mimidae), lyre-birds (Menuridae) and some members of the starling family (Sturnidae), regularly imitate the voices of other species. For example, the vocalization of the lyre-bird *Menura novae-hollandiae* is reported to borrow 80 per cent of its calls from other species; for instance, it

The song dialects of the American white-crowned sparrow (*Zonotrichia leucophrys*) have been thoroughly investigated. The sonograms of songs of three Californian populations represent an objective document of acoustic differences between the local dialects.

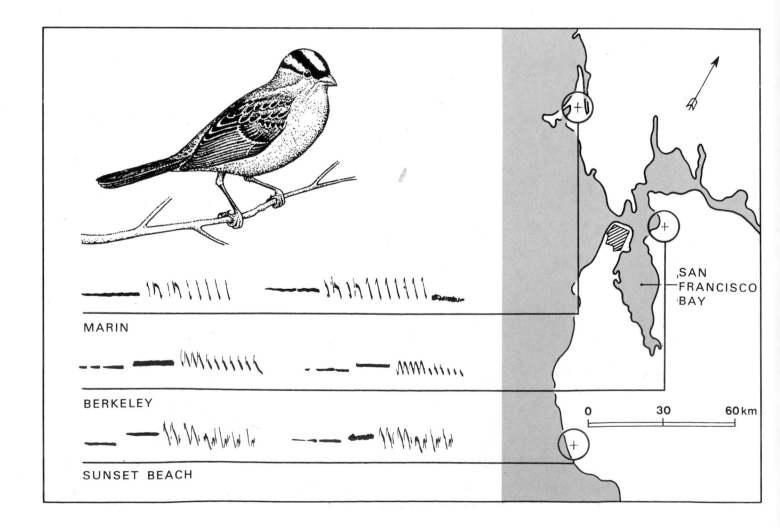

MARIN

BERKELEY

SUNSET BEACH

SAN FRANCISCO BAY

0   30   60 km

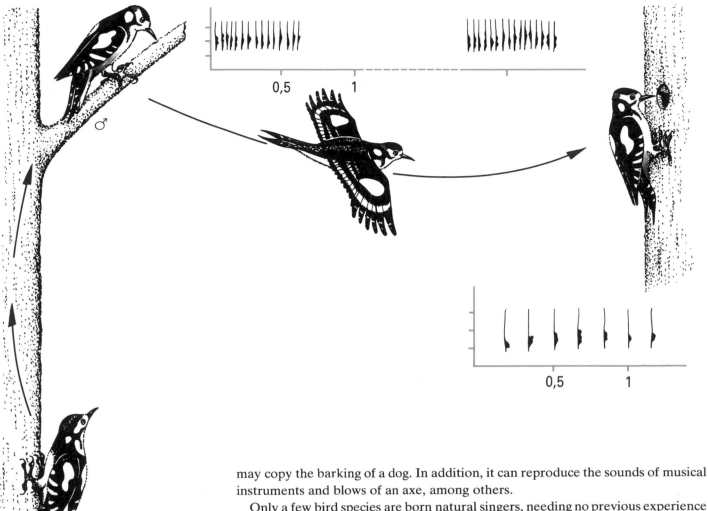

may copy the barking of a dog. In addition, it can reproduce the sounds of musical instruments and blows of an axe, among others.

Only a few bird species are born natural singers, needing no previous experience or training. The cuckoo, for example, does not have to learn its 'coo-coo', nor the turtle dove its equally simple ocarina-like call. Males of these species inherit their voices.

If we concentrate our attention on one particular seagull nesting colony, we can see that the same male gull always returns to the same spot to defend it against intruders. For safety reasons, places in the centre of the colony are more valuable than those on the periphery. A male gull gives out a loud, harsh voice from its chosen spot on the nesting ground. Ornithologists have named it the 'long call' and assume its function is territorial. A calling bird drops his wings a little, and stretches his neck forward. Both his voice and posture indicate to the other birds that 'this place is occupied'. If the defended spot attracts the attention of another male, the defender will assume an 'upright display' — stretching his neck upward and holding his beak in readiness for attack. Should the intruder choose not to respect this admonition, the calling bird issues a final warning by assuming the 'forward display' — holding the body parallel to the ground with his beak aimed directly at his opponent. The next step in this conflict is outright battle. The birds strike each other with their beaks and wrestle with their wings. This kind of territorial behaviour can be seen only in spring, when seagull nesting colonies are being established.

Birds are not the only ones who define and protect their territory acoustically. Monkeys and apes also profit from vocal communication. Some of the greatest bawlers on earth are South American howler monkeys (Alouattinae), which have

Woodpeckers have developed a special way of delineating their territories by sound. The males drum vigorously with their beaks on a hollow branch or other resonant objects. The sharp rat-a-tat-tat can be heard a long distance. In urban areas, some birds have learned to take advantage of human technology. They make their staccato sound by hammering on tin roofs, gutters or drainpipes. If a male woodpecker succeeds in attracting a female by his drumming, he will show her the way to the nest hole by his conspicuous display flight and indicate its entrance by knocking on the trunk. The sonograms reveal how the two sounds differ in their rhythms.

17

The song of gibbons (*Hylobates*) is more pleasing to the human ear than that of some other apes. Gibbons are monogamous and usually have a family of four young. The family territories are demarcated by singing, but the voice alone is not sufficient to discourage an intruder. Gibbons must give the message 'look at me when I am talking to you', and display themselves in an obvious spot. The songs of each parent are distinctive from one another. The mother's tune carries the more complex melody and apparently plays a more important role in marking the family domain. Close relatives of the gibbons, the siamangs (*Symphalangus*) (in the picture), inflate special hairless air sacs under the chin. The pleasant song of the siamangs can be heard from quite a long distance. Orang-utan (*Pongo*) males can also sing bold and lengthy songs, using a special air reservoir in their chests.

Male frogs have only a small mating territory, but they vocally defend it with the help of air sacs to intensify their voices, as illustrated by the male of *Rana esculenta*.

evolved a greatly enlarged larynx. Their throats swell into resonating drums. Howlers live in groups of about 15 individuals, and each group defends its own territory. The boundaries of neighbours do not overlap. However, the group often roves from place to place, taking over a new territory. The group announces its arrival with a thundering chorus from the adult males, being probably some of the most impressive song makers one could hear in a jungle. They give enthusiastic and unforgettable morning and afternoon performances, which can be heard more frequently when the countryside is more densely populated.

The formation of communal territories is also the habit among Colobus monkeys (Colobinae). The area taken up by a group of 5 to 20 animals may be some 60 acres. These monkeys always occupy the same tree top galleries, just under the canopy of the forest. Unlike howlers, who are seldom seen but definitely heard, Colobus monkeys regularly appear to their neighbours. This behaviour may compensate for the lower volume of their grunting voice. However, they also produce choruses on awakening, later when moving to their grazing site, and again before putting up for the night. To make it easier to recognize individual territories, one group takes up the singing when the other group stops. The dominant male is the lead singer, with backing from some of the females. During the performance, the monkeys leap from one branch to another, or they sit on visible perches and swing their long white tails. This behaviour serves as an example of combined territorial signals, both acoustic and optical.

The kingdom of a pride of lions may cover 150 to 400 square kilometres, but even such a large territory is acoustically marked. The roar of an adult lion can be heard from a distance of eight kilometres. A similarly large area is covered by the territorial calls of some seals. The loudest voice of all animals is that of the whales. The humpback whales (*Megaptera novae-angliae*) are famous for their intricate songs as they follow their regular migration routes in the ocean. These melodies gradually vary from year to year. Due to the horizontal acoustic conductivity of certain water layers, these majestic songs can allegedly be heard thousands of kilometres away. Some predatory whales use their deafening cries as a hunting weapon, to disable and even deafen their prey. However, the biological functions of most whale vocalizations still remain a mystery.

The deer buck in rut advertizes his presence and strength with a mighty roar. His age and physical abilities are reflected in the pitch and intensity of his voice. A territorial male has a strong voice that carries for hundreds of metres. The call of younger bucks is weaker and has a higher pitch. Even the youngest males occasionally vocalize, but their hoarse squealing is not taken seriously. Conversely, very old bucks can bellow only in a low-pitched voice.

A distinctive method of sound production was devised by animals living near water. They beat the water surface, producing a loud splash. The male beaver slaps the water with his tail, the crocodile with his head.

Even the 'dumb' fish provide a wealth of examples of the acoustic marking of their underwater boundaries, particularly on the coral reefs.

To be complete, our survey of acoustic territorial signals must include the insects. Quite a few species exhibit territorial behaviour. Those using the voice for this purpose include crickets, grasshoppers, katydids and cicadas. Their vocalizations are called stridulation. Males use it mainly for distributing themselves equally over the available space and for communication with their mates. The stridulation in beetles can also act as an acoustic announcement that the territory has been taken.

Flags, escutcheons and coats-of-arms have always symbolized human territories, whether it be countries or counties, dominions or estates, country clubs or tree houses. Nature was millions of years ahead of us, however, in developing a similar system of symbols. Does not the coral reef fish on this page look like a beautiful flag? Its body shape, conspicuous colours and optical dazzle are a heraldry with which the fish patrols its territory. It is not its size that commands the respect of other fish, but rather its contrasting colours. Such fish are showy and really stand out. Like a good poster, they are difficult to overlook. That is why Professor Konrad Lorenz aptly calls them the poster fish. Their visual signals only work for them during daylight hours; they lose their colouration at night.

Visual advertisement is common in many animal groups, notably in birds. The gay or variegated colours of many males are, by themselves, sufficient indicators that a male is present in the territory. If an intruder fails to heed a tenant's warning song, he will find that his colouration is a provocation for attack. This was demonstrated by another famous ethologist, Professor Niko Tinbergen, in his study of the robin (*Erithacus rubecula*). When the professor placed a tuft of red feathers into a male robin's territory, the bird furiously and repeatedly attacked the bright plumes. The same robin completely ignored a stuffed male decoy whose red feathers had been removed from its breast. The red spot, called a sign stimulus, releases the instinctive aggressive behaviour.

WHY THE STICKLEBACK HATES RED BUSES

Optical signals

The red breast feathers of the European robin (*Erithacus rubecula*) male act as the key stimulus in evoking aggressive behaviour in a male opponent.

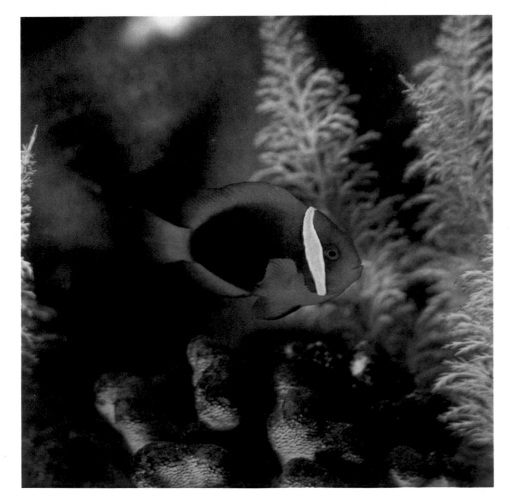

The clown fish from the genus *Amphiprion* lives in a well-protected territory — between the stinging tentacles of a large sea anemone. The fish is protected against the paralytic effects of its venom with a thick layer of mucus.

19

The coral fish of the genus *Pomacentrus.*

A similar sign stimulus, the red belly of another male, enrages the stickleback fish (*Gasterosteus aculeatus*). His rage increases when the effigy is placed in a position with its head pointed down. In fish language this means a threat. Professor Tinbergen observed that even a red bus passing by the window of the laboratory made the stickleback males in their tanks go into a frenzy. Fortunately, the fish will hardly ever encounter a similar false signal in the wild.

Birds not endowed with gay colours accentuate their presence in the territory by ostentatious display flights, particularly if a stranger appears. Buzzards, hawks and skylarks do this. A very typical display flight is also performed by the males of the Eurasian brown tree-pipit (*Anthus trivialis*). The male usually surveys his territory from the top of a tall solitary tree. At regular intervals, he takes off on a flight path slanting upward, while vigorously singing. After reaching a certain height, he stops singing, spreads his wings, and glides downward while producing a series of long 'tseeya — tseeya' whistles.

Still another group of birds makes particularly good use of optical signals. These are the domestic fowl and their wild kin — pheasants, grouse, peacocks and many others. Males are generally larger than the females, and their plumage sports party colours during the breeding season. When a male is excited and wants to threaten or intimidate his adversary, he enlarges the contours of his body by puffing up his feathers, fanning out his tail or sometimes inflating the brightly coloured, featherless wattle on his throat, as most dramatically exemplified in the satyr tragopon on the following page. Wattles are also sign stimuli for the opponent; for instance, when the male turkey sees red, it has the same effect on him as the waving of a red flag supposedly has on a bull.

'Exhibitionism' as a part of territorial behaviour is observed not only in birds. We have already mentioned some monkeys, in which visual contact is a prerequisite of efficient communication. Colobus monkeys signal by swinging their shaggy tails at their neighbours, while the males of other species threaten their opponents by

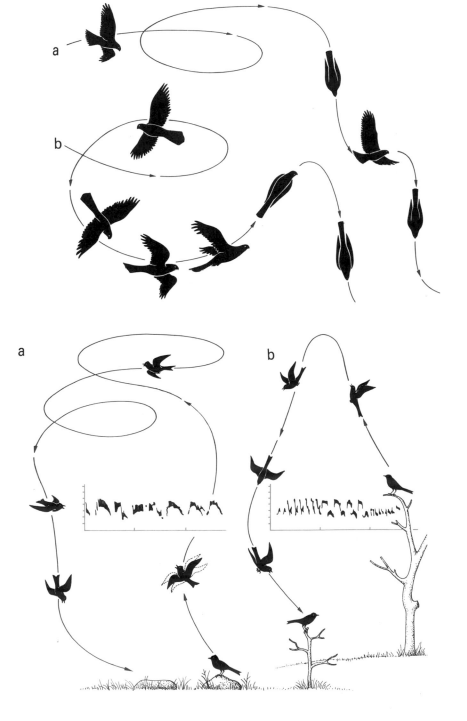

The display flights of the common buzzard (*Buteo buteo*) (a) and the northern goshawk (*Accipiter gentilis*) (b).

The display flights of the skylark (*Alauda arvensis*) (a) and the tree pipit (*Anthus trivialis*) (b) with sonograms of their territorial songs.

The satyr tragopan (*Tragopan satyra*) male displays his colourful featherless wattle mainly for his mate during courtship. During territorial disputes he also uses his optical weapon to intimidate his opponents. This alpine Tibetan gallinaceous bird lives in monogamous pairs.

exposing gaily coloured genitals or the conspicuously coloured hair on their inner thighs. Buffaloes and some antelopes claim the ownership of a territory by placing themselves like statues on an elevated spot in the pasture. The marine lizards, iguanas, have a crest of large scales along their spine. Males display it in territorial competition to appear grand and formidable.

The degree of satyr's excitement is reflected in the size of his wattle.

Less conspicuous but even more cunning are the optical marks used by many mammals to protect their territories. It is amazing how diverse their means may be for this purpose. A favourite method is marking with feaces, particularly in the dog family. The animal usually places its mark on a stone, stump, tussock or other elevated spot along the path, so that it can hardly be overlooked. Dog owners know all too well how long it takes their pet to find a suitable place to relieve itself.

Marking the vegetation is another device which can be used for optically announcing one's presence in a territory. If the bark of a tree is stripped off, conspicuous white spots apear on the trunk or branches. Bears, pandas, European buffaloes, roebucks and squirrels use their claws, horns, antlers or teeth to make such visible signs. Bears and buffaloes enhance their marks by applying the scent of their urine to them in a special way: they wallow in their urine, then rub their backs against the mark. Wild pigs and deer rub mud onto tree trunks and add urine scent to the mark. Large cats such as the jaguar (*Panthera onca*), leopard (*P. pardus*) and tiger (*P. tigris*) leave claw marks on tree bark, on the ground along their pathways, or on solitary rocks. Roebucks remove turf in prominent places within their domain, creating distinct bare spots. Even a well-trodden path becomes an optical mark in itself.

Many peaceful and carefree-looking male butterflies are actually staunch defenders of their territory. The size of their province greatly varies according to the species. Perhaps the largest territories belong to members of the North American swallowtail *Papilio zelicaon*. Males of this species claim ownership of entire hilltops. Much smaller areas are defended by some European butterflies, which use these spots as mating places. Males of the speckled wood butterfly (*Pararge aegeria*) compete in a sparse deciduous forest for mere sunspots on the

Nuptial aggregations of insects on hilltops and mountain crests are a phenomenon known to entomologists as hilltopping. Besides butterflies, hilltopping is often exhibited by the flesh-flies (Sarcophagidae) or warbler-flies (Hypodermatidae).

Anolis lizard males flaunt a crest of brightly coloured skin on their chests made taut by the erection of their hyoid bone. The colour of the crest differs according to species, which is a helpful adaptation where more than one species live together on one tree. When two males meet each other, they introduce themselves by throwing out their chests. When the colour of their 'passports' match, a conflict is inevitable.

ground. Experiments performed with this species indicate that the resident has a home advantage over the visitor in such encounters. When the original owner was removed by the entomologist, his spot was soon taken by another male. When the former resident was then released, a fight ensued. The winner was usually the new owner, despite his relatively new claim on the area. However, when both contestants 'consider' themselves to be the rightful owners, the conflict escalates to a more serious fight.

Some readers may wonder how the fragile butterflies can fight. The answer was provided by another European species, the small tortoiseshell (*Aglais urticae*). The encounter of the two males consists of rapid horizontal chases, interspersed with swift spiralling climbs, during which the rivals leapfrog over each other, each trying to attain and maintain a position above the other. When one achieves this dominant position, the loser dives and another horizontal chase takes place. The pair may travel up to 200 metres from the territory before one male eventually breaks away and returns. The fight is really a symbolic contest in which the rivals evaluate each other by comparing their manoeuvrability.

The aerial duels of dragonflies and damselflies have similar symbolic meaning. The male defends a certain space above a lake or pond which is suitable for laying eggs. He patrols his territory incessantly, for he will not tolerate a rival there. Any flying object provokes him to respond swiftly, even a paper ball tossed into his flight path. If a male of his own species encroaches upon his territory, a fight invariably occurs. Since the predatory dragonflies are equipped with large mandibles, a real combat would have fatal consequences for one or both fighters. For this reason, physical encounters are used rarely, as a last resort, when comparison of strength by threat displays fails. Dragonflies have conspicuously coloured abdomens, with which the males exhibit their species identity. They also show their colours as an emphatic banner of scorn for intruders. This was shown in an experiment in which males, whose original colour patterns were painted over, enjoyed significantly less favour with females. They were less successful in defending their territory, and therefore the females paid little attention to these property-less males.

Males of the American dragonfly *Plathemis lydia* try to intimidate each other by displaying their white backs. If one experimentally paints the abdomen of a male black, the other males will ignore him.

Scent marking is an almost universal means of communication in mammals. We humans were the only ones to be short-changed, having noses endowed with relatively low sensitivity to chemical stimuli. Hence, we are not privy to many of the secrets of scent language which other animals use. We can only detect pieces of indirect evidence which suggest the wealth and variety of scent signals. Our understanding of the function of this special vocabulary is more often a subject of mere conjecture or wild guesses than one of direct experimental evidence.

Characteristic and conspicuous behaviour usually accompanies scent marking. Until recently, it was thought that territoriality was the only purpose for such marking. The prevailing opinion was that these marks were a warning signal to keep other animals out of the marked area, acting as fences of scent. A fresh mark was supposed to mean 'stop', a less fresh one 'proceed cautiously', and an old mark to declare 'you may safely continue'. However, new experimental studies and field observations of many animal species do not provide much firm evidence to support these opinions.

It appears that scent marking has many more functions than previously supposed, and it occurs even in animals that are not territorial, such as, for instance, rhinoceroses. Moreover, the marks can be found all over the territory and not just on the boundaries. If an animal is transferred from its own territory to an unfamiliar place, it will continue scent marking there. Alien marks are not usually avoided; on the contrary, they are given much attention and are inspected thoroughly. Therefore scent marks do not directly deter a visitor's entry into an occupied territory. Apparently they provide a warning and probably include additional information about the resident, such as its age, sex, physical strength and other abilities, the current phase of the owner's reproductive cycle, and even whether they have met before. The scent of the animal's mark acts as his passport for individual identification. It may also form a communication bridge between two solitary animals for whom there would otherwise be little chance of meeting, rather like an advertisement in the personal column of a newspaper.

If the intruder comes with a conqueror's intentions, then it depends on his inclinations and previous experience whether the signal will intimidate him. He will probably respect the scented 'no trespassing' sign only after he has lost the first encounter fight. The resident of the territory is always the more strongly motivated one in this first encounter. His self-assurance is supported by the presence of his own scent all over his property. The scent mark is a 'hallmark' of his home. Zoo attendants are well acquainted with the habit many mammals have of intensively marking their cages or runs after the area has been cleaned, and they get exasperated when the animal's mark happens to be faeces. From the animal's point of view, however, the absence of its own scent is stressful and may evoke abnormal behaviour and even sterility.

In some cases, territorial scenting may act as a temporary threat signal, given off to intimidate the opponent. The 'stink fights' of the lemurs may serve as an example. When two males meet to dispute their territorial claims, the first thing they do is to perfume their long, hairy tails with a blend of secretions from the scent glands in their forearms. With their weapons 'loaded', they stand in opposition with their tails curved forward over their backs, furiously fanning their personal odour at the opponent. The fight may last up to an hour. Its outcome depends not only on the intensity of the scent, but also on the relative size of the contestants, for the ritual is also a visual display.

A method universally used by mammals is scent marking with urine. The scenting individual often urinates sparingly, in small portions, as if to make it last longer. This technique is best known in the dog family, where it has not been suppressed even by thousands of years of domestication. Indeed, a thoroughbred dog on a leash cannot restrain himself when it comes to this social obligation toward his four-legged fellows, however embarrassing it may be for his master. Foxes and wolves behave similarly. The latter possess group territories and jointly defend their common ground against the members of strange packs.

Even that typical act of raising the hindleg is supposed to have a communicatory meaning. It is believed that the higher the dog places his mark, the more dominant the status he achieves among the local dog population. If this is true, then I have to admire the way that a tiny chihuahua in our neighborhood cured his inferiority complex: he did a 'handstand' on his forelegs while urinating. In the squirrel monkeys (*Saimiri*) this is the regular marking posture.

Prosimii (lemurs, lorises, tarsiers etc.) and some Old World monkeys that live in the trees scent mark with their urine in a special way. The animal releases a drop of urine on the foot of a foreleg and then smears it onto the other feet. Then as it walks on branches, it automatically leaves a message concerning its presence wherever it goes. Such scent stamps are left behind by the galagos and bushbabies (*Galago*), aye-ayes (*Daubentonia*), capuchins (*Cebus*) and many other lower primates. The scent of their urine is usually mixed with the odour of their dermal glands, and the resulting blend serves as an identification mark.

Some social animals use a collective system of urine marking. Mice make urinating posts using piles of faecal pellets stuck together with urine. These are distributed along the main communication routes within the colony. Individuals of either sex rub their urogenital regions on these posts, leaving behind mucus containing proteins and fatty acids. This secretion is broken down by bacteria, which further increases the smell of the posts and gives them the 'proper' scent.

Wolves also have the social duty of maintaining urinating posts. All members of the pack take care of these posts by regularly renewing them, often waiting in line to take their turn at contributing to the mark. In winter, the marking post creates a tall golden cone of frozen urine, which is a particularly striking sight when found in the middle of a lake. For strangers, it certainly gives clear-cut information about territory and size of the pack.

The use of faecal pellets as an optical mark has already been mentioned. Even our insensitive noses can usually detect that these pellets also serve as olfactory marks, especially since the scent is often exaggerated by musky secretions of the anal glands. It is not by chance that we find the smell intrudes on our senses most prominently at the zoo. Members of the dog, cat and marten families have particularly well-developed anal scent glands. European polecats and North American skunks even use their musky secretions as a defence weapon. Otters mark their exits from the water with faeces too. If no suitable stone is available for the purpose, they pile up mud and place their mark at the top. Another member of the marten family, the African striped weasel (*Poecilogale albinucha*), sticks its faeces on vertical surfaces. Even the scent of rabbit pellets is a territorial signal for the colony.

Besides these kinds of animal conversation, which by our standards are bad smelling, there are some that are less offensive to our noses. A variety of dermal glands in different parts of the body contribute to communication. In mammals alone, over 40 kinds of these glands have been described. Not all, however, are employed for territorial marking. In the most studied laboratory rodents, dermal scent glands were found on virtually every part of their bodies: on flanks, belly, feet, at the base of the tail, and even on the face. The animal rubs different parts of its body, depending on the context, on surrounding objects in order to leave various messages. In the lining of rabbits' cheeks there are submandibular glands which

Members of the cat family assume their own characteristic posture when marking with urine. They turn their back toward the object to be marked and spray it high. One can observe this in the house cat as well as in the tiger.

have a territorial function. While the rabbit grazes on grass, these gland secretions are left behind to mark its realm. Bats also have rather unusual locations for their scent glands: on their lips, chest and wings.

An equally impressive repertoire of scent glands has been described in antlered game animals. Deer have them around the flag of their tails, on their bellies, heels, and even on the velvet that covers their antlers, as well as at the antler base. When a buck peels the velvet from his antlers by scratching them against trees, he leaves behind his scent. Other large glands are in the dermal slits under a deer's eyes.

When the roebuck peels the velvet from his new antlers, he scrapes bark from small tree trunks and branches, thus making an optical mark. The mark is then perfumed by secretions from his forehead glands.

The roebuck has his scent glands on the forehead (a), around the tail (b), on his heels (c) and between the hind hoofs (d).

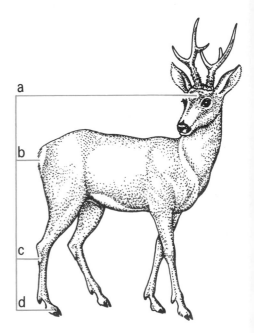

These pre-orbital glands are equipped with muscles with which they can be opened wide, enabling transference of secretions from the glands onto twigs. The deer can also use these slits to express its mood with an optical signal, blinking them open and shut as we do eyelids.

Some scent marking antelopes look as if they are trying to poke out their eyes. They dip thorns, grass stems or twigs into the gland in front of their eyes, as a pen into an inkpot. The secretions left behind serve as a territorial signal.

We could go on enumerating the ways by which one animal leaves his cachet as a testimony of its presence for the benefit of others. We could speak in detail about the olfactory marks of lizards, or the numerous sources of smell in the fur of monkeys. We might talk at length about the mysterious temple gland of elephants, the secretions of which mature males rub on tree-trunks or termite nests and whose increased activity forebodes a period of intolerance and aggression in this giant. However, only surmises and conjectures have been made concerning the function and significance of all these signals. Before closing this chapter, let us have a short excursion into the microworld of insects.

The males of many solitary wasps are also quite possessive of their territory. They perch on prominent places on vegetation, on solitary stumps or on tree trunks

Examples of scent-marking in mammals. The male blackbuck (*Antilope cervicarpa*) (a) marks the twigs with the secretion of his orbital gland, the pigmy hippopotamus (*Choeropsis liberiensis*) (b) spreads its own faeces with its tail and the male chamois (*Rupicapra rupicapra*) (c) rubs his scent glands, which are situated behind the horns, on the branches.

near the plants that females visit for food. There they vigorously elbow out all competition. The finer their location, the better their prospects for meeting a mate. This explains why the males fight so adamantly each morning for the first-rate perches and why they repeatedly return to the same spot for several days, although at night they may docilely share one shelter with several other males.

Digger wasp males (Sphecidae) mark their perches with a secretion from their mandibular or abdominal glands. The male of the wasp *Eucercis flavocincta* has special brushes on the undersurface of his abdomen, which he uses when applying the scent. Mystery surrounds the territorial behaviour of orchid bees (Englossini). The males rest on tree trunks in the clearings of tropical forests. Now and then they leave their perch to make a patrol flight, but they always return to the same spot. The unanswered question is how it happens that year after year, generation after generation, males select the same perching points that their predecessors chose, never varying more than a few centimetres from the ancestral spot. What has been known for some time is that the males of these solitary bees collect nectar from orchids and perfume themselves with the blossoms' fragrance. It is supposed that this action is grooming for the benefit of females. Firm proof for this contention is still missing. It is known that a female seeks a male's mating territory by sight. His smell may be only a short-distance cue for her.

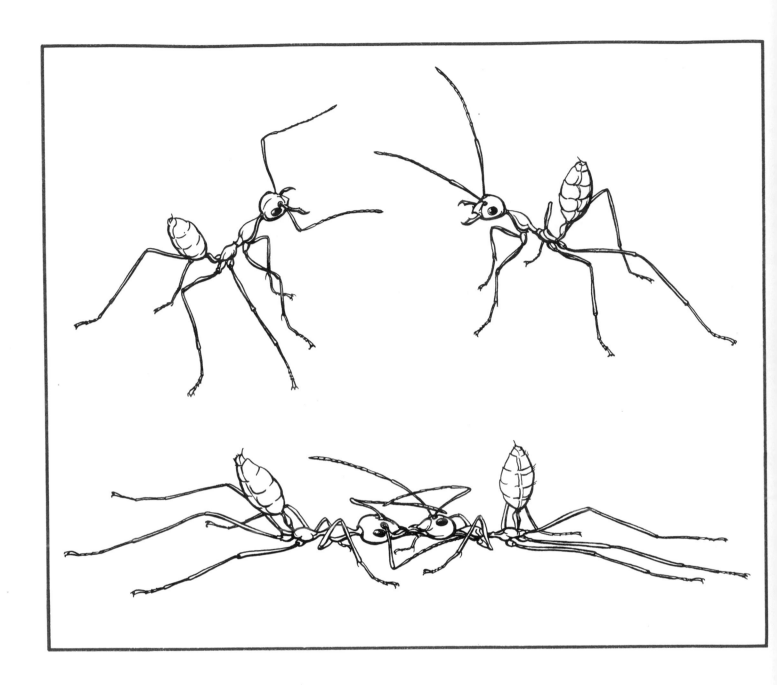

In ants, each colony possesses its own territory, and the boundaries of the estate are also marked by chemical means. Studies on weaver ants (*Oecophila longinoda*) show that worker ants use three compounds, each originating from a different gland, to mark the territory. If a scout ant pioneers new unoccupied territory, it leaves behind a fragrant trail made of a secretion from its rectal gland. The compound is a summons for the others to follow, which entomologists call the long-range recruitment pheromone. Should a worker ant encounter an alien ant, it will use another chemical, from the sternal glands on the underside of the belly, to drive away the adversary. At the same time, this compound makes an alarm call to all of its nestmates within a range of several centimetres. This fragrant entreaty, which brings help in subduing the intruder, is known as a short-range recruitment pheromone. Finally, when the territory is well secured, the ants excrete a territorial pheromone from their anal glands, which induces self-confident behaviour in the

Before two weaver ant workers attack each other during a territorial dispute, they perform threat displays.

30

The weaver ant worker (*Oecophila longinoda*) normally runs with her abdomen elevated (1). When inspecting an unfamiliar territory she lays a scent trail behind (2), which is made of rectal gland secretions (a). When endangered (3), the ant calls for help by means of emanations of the sternal gland secretions (b), which are laid in the form of a looping trail. (Enlarged tips of the abdomen are shown in the insets.)

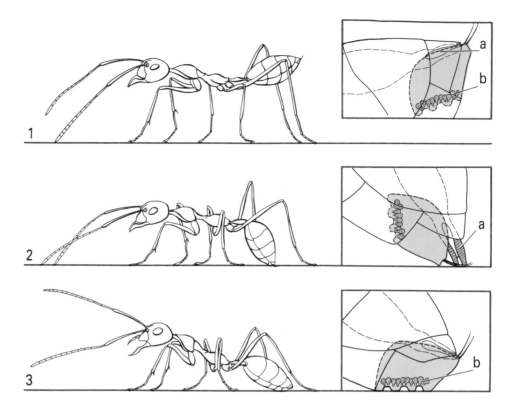

Male bumblebees are territorial. The function of their scent marks for delineation of their spheres of interest was not only proven, but Swedish scientists even chemically identified their perfumes. The margins of leaves and blades of grass are marked with a secretion from the male bumblebee's mandibular glands during his patrol rounds. A young queen on her nuptial flight may pause at one of these fragrant beacons and wait for his return, but other males are deterred by his scent.

residents. This gives them the composure they need to call for help and retreat only reluctantly when overwhelmed. Out of the range of this smell, on a strange territory, their behaviour is far more cautious and uncertain. Only ants of the same species but from different colonies are put off by the territorial pheromone of their neighbours.

Weaver ants are arboreal, and their territory may consist of one or more trees. They build their nests in the tree's crown by weaving clusters of leaves together. However, let us not be misled by their name, which denotes a peaceful occupation. These weavers are ferocious predators that attack any living thing on their occupied tree. The ancient Chinese culture knew about their territorial habits as early as 300 A.D. and took advantage of it for biological control of insect pests. The peasants transferred branches with weaver ant nests to their orchards. This method is still used successfully in Ghana to protect cocoa plantations. The occurrence of virus diseases that are transferred by leaf bugs is surprisingly reduced on plants protected by the ants.

LOOKING FOR A MATE

The mating season brings several additional concerns to animals. First of all, they must find a mate of the same species, and of the opposite sex. The problem is not always as straightforward as it might seem. If it was, the animals would not have had to evolve such profuse and intricate means of advertising themselves and their species identity, and of preventing their wasting time and energy on the wrong species.

Another problem the would-be parents have to face is to select a first rate partner, since not all members of one's species are ideal mates. Stronger and healthier individuals have a better chance of producing more eggs, and of acquiring and defending a larger and more fertile territory, which enables them to provide more offspring with food. Hence, it is in the interest of each individual to choose a partner with the greatest reproduction potential. This need stands out especially in those species that stage communal courtships. Within groups of males (and on rare occasions in females), rivalry and competition takes place at the beginning of the mating season, with the aim of testing the qualities of the contestants. This gives the opposite sex something by which to judge when making their choice.

The task is not over, however, when the right mate is found. The new partners must overcome their inherent aggressive tendencies in order to engage in more intimate contact and to avert misunderstandings which may lead to an unhappy end. This is essential in well armed predatory species. Furthermore, the couple generally need to synchronize their reproductive cycles with each other, as well as with environmental conditions, so that the climax of their relationship — mating — will occur under optimum circumstances, at the right time and place. Realization of all these goals is often the result of elaborate and conspicuous behaviour that has caught the attention and piqued the curiosity of people for ages. Ethologists call it courtship.

WHY DO FURRY HUSBANDS SWING MORE THAN THE FEATHERY ONES?

The mating systems

In the sexual context, if we look at animals in terms of our own moral standards, some of them fall into the category of exemplary husbands, others deserve the label of promiscuous philanderers, still others are sultans of large harems. We would also find swinging singles, old maids, grass widows and regular widows or widowers past their prime. There is, however, no reason to praise one, take umbrage at another, or be sorry for some. Behaviour associated with reproduction, called epigamic behaviour, is one of the fundamental characteristics of each species. It reflects the social organization of the animals as it evolved throughout the ages in a way that best suits the ecological requirements of their species.

When both partners are kept busy with the rearing of offspring, as is the case for instance in swans, wild geese and cranes, the male and the female make monogamous bonds, which means that each breeding individual mates with only one partner. Both partners are equally equipped to look after the young. In birds, such an arrangement occurs in 90 per cent of cases. Lifelong faithfulness to each other is called perennial monogamy. Divorce will happen only if one partner fails to fulfil its duties. The marital bonds are maintained even between the breeding seasons. Therefore, choosing the best mate is especially important for these birds which stay with the same partner for a period of years. A genuinely permanent pair bond is found in long-lived birds. Albatrosses, gannets, gulls, swans, wild geese and cranes are examples of this lifestyle. Most other bird groups maintain seasonal monogamy, bonding only during the breeding period and living apart during the rest of the year. This category encompasses many migratory birds. Each spring, both partners have a compulsion to return to the exact site of last year's nest and hence the pair usually gets together year after year.

Monogamy is, however, rather an exceptional arrangement in the majority of animal groups. More often, an individual is polygamous, mating with two or more partners. Commonly, one male fathers the offspring of several females, which is

Turning up their beaks is also a greeting gesture in a pair of storks. This ceremony can be seen when a partner returns to the nest with the prey.

The male of the largest European bird, the giant bustard (*Otis tarda*), looks equally excited whether threatening his rival or courting his mate.

called polygyny. Far less frequently, one female may have two or more faithful husbands and this is called polyandry. Polyandry in birds can only occur under certain circumstances and the sex roles become reversed in its extreme form. The female defends a territory, courts the male and leaves him to incubate the eggs and care for the brood. Her plumage is usually more conspicuous than that of the male. The northern jacana (*Jacana spinosa*), a shorebird found from Texas to Costa Rica, is the only bird species known to maintain several males simultaneously. In other polyandrous birds, the female, having laid one clutch, leaves it with the father and looks for another male to fertilize her second clutch. The mating system of this kind can be found, for example, in spotted sandpiper (*Actitis macularia*), whose female can lay up to five clutches, each being fathered by another male. Needless to say that polyandry is a particularly useful adaptation for reproduction in near Arctic latitudes, where summer is short but numbers of insects to feed on are enormous. In these conditions one bird can incubate a clutch alone since it can collect food quickly enough to return to the nest before the eggs have chilled fatally. This method multiplies the reproductive potential of species which would otherwise only have time to rear one brood during their short breeding season. It should be emphasized that the males of the polyandrous species are truly faithful husbands to their mates. On the contrary, in promiscuous species there are no pair bonds, and both males and females mate with more than one member of the opposite sex.

Why are the polygynous systems so popular in the animal kingdom? Probably one reason is the lack of 'liberation' among the females. A polygynous system is

really feasible only when all the burden of parental care is carried by the female. Let us take the evolutionarily advanced order of mammals as an example. Typically, a mammalian father contributes only with his genes. The mother provides everything else. She nurtures the growing embryo in her womb, produces milk to feed the young and warms and protects her helpless offspring. To somehow compensate for her enormous investment of energy, she has a great privilege. It is she who usually chooses the father for her offspring. Indiscretion in choosing a mate has more serious consequences for her than for the male. If she mates with a male who carries a genetic abnormality resulting in high mortality of her offspring, the female may miss a whole season's breeding opportunity. Should the male make the same mistake, he loses only the amount of energy invested in courting and mating the defective female. He will still have ample opportunity to make up for his loss by mating with many normal females.

These differences in the risk resulting from the choice of a wrong partner explain why females are so coy and choosy during courtship, and why they let males go through their paces with displays and competitions. Only by comparing the males'

Males of the black grouse (*Lyrurus tetrix*) come to the lek before dawn, immediately beginning a fierce competition for small bits of land, which are symbolic mating territories.

One of the most bizarre rituals among gallinaceous birds is performed by the North American sage grouse (*Centrocercus urophasianus*) of the Rocky Mountains. Within three seconds, the male puffs out his oesophageal sac twice while emitting a loud popping sound.

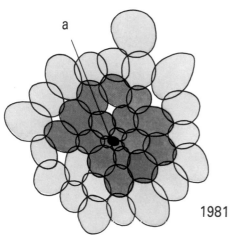

1981

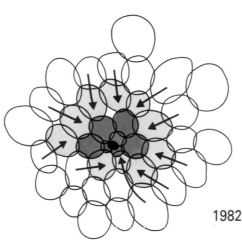

1982

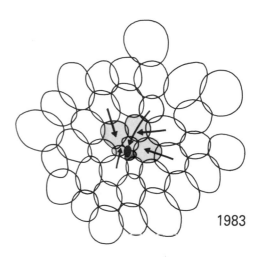

1983

demonstrations of their biological qualities can the female select the best and most able suitor, irrespective of the number of females with whom she may have to share him.

Polygyny does exist in birds, although rarely and only in those species whose fledglings are well developed prior to emerging from the egg. In such cases the parents do not have to feed the young themselves, and the few parental duties can be assumed by the female alone. The males are usually endowed with striking plumage, as represented by the gallinaceous birds such as grouse, pheasants and quail. Their audacious colouration serves to intimidate their rivals and to attract and impress the females. Courtship is a communal affair for them, and the selection of mates takes place year after year in exactly the same locations, called leks.

Each lek is divided into a number of small symbolic territories. The most intense fights are for territories in the middle of the lek, since ownership of such a central site signifies the dominant status of the male. Hens gather around the lek at dawn to select a mate according to two criteria: they are attracted to the successful fighters who hold central territories, and to males with the most refined technique of courtship. Thus the female picks not only the strongest cocks, but also the most polite and attentive ones, if you will excuse the anthropomorphisms. This is not by chance, since politeness can only be acquired through experience. As a result, the oldest cocks win the most hens. These are the ones which have demonstrated their fitness, their superiority in fighting, and proven their fundamental ability to survive longer.

The owners of the central territories on the lek (a) attract the most females for mating among grouse and their kin. Idealized diagrams of the symbolic territories show that young cocks (marked blue) are not successful in defending the most valuable spots during their first breeding season. They will gain better positions only in the second and particularly in the third breeding season, if they survive.

BUTTERFLY ON THE MERRY-GO-ROUND

Visual courtship cues

'Slim architect, 30, 6'2'', Aquarian, wants to meet slender, good-looking blonde, under 25. Photo appreciated, box 2312.'

Countless advertisements like this appear in the personal columns of newspapers around the world. They demonstrate how important it is that the potential lover be pleasing to our eyes. Let us not deliberate here about whether the contemporary ideal of beauty is necessarily the most successful for the reproduction of the human species. Certainly the rest of the animal kingdom has a practical aesthetic judgement.

Animals active during daylight often make use of their good vision to exploit all kinds of optical communication signals when looking for a mate and also for the more intimate situations that follow. Sight plays a role of utmost importance in birds. The showy adornments and elegant plumage of male grouse, pheasants, turkeys and peacocks have developed not only for the intimidation of rivals at the leks — communal mating grounds — but also to attract the hens and persuade them of their cocks' finer qualities. Good looks are certainly an important criterion used by females when they assess their suitors, for this has been proven experimentally with the domestic fowl. Researchers changed the colouration of a brown leghorn cock by adding white feathers to the brown plumage on his neck. This previously

The calling males of the turkey (*Meleagris gallopavo*) and the capercaillie (*Tetrao urogallus*).

successful wooer lost his charisma in the eyes of hens of his breed, even though his love technique did not suffer by the revamping he was given. The experiment demonstrated that hens discriminate among would-be mates by the comparative appearance of the males rather than by any variations of courtship displays.

Charles Darwin concluded that the radical difference in appearance between males and females and the ostentatious behaviours of the males (both called secondary sex characteristics) serve to satisfy female whims. The hen's bias towards the male's splendorous attire explains the evolution of sexual dimorphism. The male's eye-catching dress is a luxury which hardly contributes to his longevity. The gay colours, various trimmings and large size increase his chances with the females, but at the same time make him a conspicuous target for predators. However, in polygynous species the male has no choice. Countless generations of his ancestors competed in beauty pageants, and the current state is a result of only the most conspicuous, best developed and most assertive becoming fathers. A conservatively dressed male might live twice as long, but what use would it be for the propagation of the species to harbour homely bachelors which leave no offspring?

The courtship display of the greater bird of paradise (*Paradisea apoda*) from New Guinea.

The female Australian lyre-birds (Menuridae) and birds of paradise (Paradiseidae) also seem to be fascinated by their suitors' magnificent feathers. The male lyre-bird makes his display on the forest floor, where he has cleared a 'dancing' space for the purpose. While vocalizing loudly, he throws his gorgeous tail over his head as a lacy veil. An equally unforgettable experience is witnessing the courtship display of the birds of paradise. The males perform on carefully selected branches from which they have removed all the foliage so that the sun can illuminate their glittering dress when they go on stage. They show off their magnificent colours and the remarkable structure of their feathers in most bizarre postures. The male of the blue bird of paradise (*Paradisea rudolphi*) hangs upside down, with his sky-blue feathers fanned out, producing the whirring sound of a mechanical toy. It is hard to realize that this is a living creature.

Another wonder of Australia is the bowerbird (Ptilonorhynchidae). Since the males lack spectacular plumage, they artfully win female attention in their own unique way. From straws and twigs, the male constructs an elaborate edifice which will never serve as the family nest. Instead, this bower is a trysting place designed to attract as many partners of the fair sex as possible for mating. The decoration of this structure is highly ingenious.

The bowerbirds of New Guinea decorate the walls of their bowers with colourful wing-cases of beetles or with flowers, replacing the faded blossoms with fresh ones. They also collect bones, shells and bits of glass to pile at the entrance of their bowers. The building of such a monumental construction takes several months, and the owner must defend it against other males. Different species of bowerbirds are attracted by different colours. While the satin bowerbird (*Ptilonorhynchus violaceus*) collects only blue objects, the spotted bowerbird (*Chlamydera maculata*) prefers white ones. The male entices the female by singing, and when she comes closer he coaxes her into the entrance. While the female inspects the portal on one side, he quickly runs around to the other doorway and flaunts the bright purple or yellow feathers on the back of his neck to beguile her into stepping inside. Immediately upon entering, their passion is so great that quite often the magnificent edifice cannot stand the commotion.

Transferring all of a male's attractiveness to inanimate and beautiful objects is a unique case in the animal kingdom. The male exhausts all his reproductive ardour in making the bower, and therefore takes little care in constructing the actual nest and bringing up the young. As a matter of fact, the bower building is a modified instinct of the nest construction, and the collection of colourful objects is a modified instinct of the feeding of the nestlings. Indeed, it has been observed that the bowerbird brings food to his bower and 'feeds' his treasures.

The male satin bowerbird (*Ptilonorhynchus violaceus*) covers the interior walls of his bower with blue paint composed of blueberry juice and his own saliva. The exterior of his dome of love is decorated with a variety of blue objects. If we add an object which does not match his mono-chromatic colour scheme, he removes it in a fit of rage.

A fritillary, *Boloria selene*.

The merry-go-round used by Dr. Magnus during his investigations of the visual orientation of the fritillaries. A male ready to mate becomes excited not only by a mechanical dummy of a female butterfly but also by a spinning spool painted orange and black.

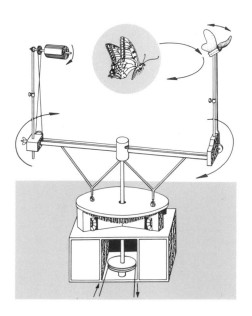

Most butterflies, also, rely on sight during courtship. The male often finds a suitable perch, from which he strikes at everything resembling a female that flutters by. He may dart at a falling leaf or at a butterfly of another species. He realizes his mistake only when he gets closer — by the sense of smell. Some 35 years ago, a German zoologist, Dr. Dietrich Magnus, demonstrated through ingenious experiments how the male silver-washed fritillary (*Argynnis paphia*) can be fooled by various visual stimuli. The scientist constructed a special two-arm merry-go-round, and at the end of each arm he placed an artificial butterfly with movable wings. The males, for whom this performance was meant, readily approached the dummies which resembled, at least distantly, the shape and colours of the female. They gave up the pursuit only when they discovered the lack of the proper smell. The apparatus deceived the males so reliably that the designer could venture to alter the shape of the models and thus follow, step-by-step, what visual characteristics excited the males most. The males responded equally well to spinning discs or triangles as to a dummy of a butterfly. What counted most, however, was the size. Smaller models elicited less interest in the males than those of the female's size. The surprising finding was that the males were still more excited by an imitation female double or even four times the natural size.

The rate of wing flutter appeared to be of similar importance. For the study of this phenomenon, Dr. Magnus simplified his models. He used a horizontally rotating spool, half of which had been painted black and half orange, which are the prevalent colours of a fritillary's wings. If the male was given a choice between a slowly rotating spool and one spinning twice as fast, he invariably preferred the faster alternations of colour. His responses increased up to the speed of 75 rotations per second. At faster rotations, he ceased to respond to the spool, because both colours fused. The same fusing happens to us at a mere 20 rotations per second. Thus Dr. Magnus discovered that an ideal female fritillary – in the eyes of a male – should be four times larger, of almost any shape, and have wings of pure orange, instead of speckled, and that flutter as fast as the male is able to perceive. Such a butterfly could live only in a fantasy land, however, because she would need to have extremely powerful muscles. It is common in nature that abnormally strong stimuli are more effective than normal ones. The commercial success of well-endowed movie stars is a good example.

In some butterflies species specific patterns may be coded in the spectral range invisible to the human eye. Thus, for example, the plain wings of the male whites (Pieridae) reflect bright specks in the ultra-violet light. The other male and female whites can see and use the patterns for species recognition, because the insect eyes are UV-sensitive.

The interspecific differences in appearance do not always have to be obvious in the visible range either. Birdwatchers know only too well how difficult it is to identify some little perching birds, such as flycatchers, warblers, pipits and American sparrows. The characteristics listed in field guides to distinguish bird species often concern quite fine details. Even these minutia can serve as a cue to the bird during courtship. Field experiments made on four gull species serve as a good example. The plumage of all these species is almost identical: the body is white, the wings and the back are grey. Yet they do not interbreed even if they nest in the same colony. The experiments proved that the sole reason for this is the difference in the colour of the eyes in the individual species.

When captured birds' eye rings were painted over, the female rarely chose a male which had the 'wrong' eye-pattern. If the makeup on the male's eye-ring was applied after he had already paired with a female, the couple's bond was not broken and they nested successfully. However, if the female had the wrong eye-colour, the male would accept and pair with her but would not go so far as to mount her. The pair usually broke up after a couple of weeks.

Males of some live-bearing (viviparous) fish introduce themselves and reveal their species identity to the female by a special courtship dance. The guppy (*Poecilia reticulata*), a popular tropical aquarium fish, is viviparous. Guppies are native to South America, where many related species may share the same pond or puddle. Females of the individual species are very similar in appearance, whereas the males differ strikingly in their patterns of body colouration. Their elaborate dances preceding mating are also species characteristic. The mating of the viviparous fish is more complicated than the spawning of oviparous (egg-laying) fish, because fertilization must take place while the eggs are still inside the female's body. To achieve this, a male guppy of the species *Poecilia reticulata* situates himself in front of the female, twists his body into an S-shape and quivers, holding this position for several seconds before attempting to mate. The male's excitement reaches its climax when he spreads wide his colourful fins. If the female is receptive (this time period being limited to only two or three days after parturition) she will allow the male to continue his intimacies. The transfer of the sperm into her anal opening is directed by the male's erected anal fin, which functions as an accessory copulatory organ.

The male of the related *P. picta* courts the female in a different way. He literally

The nuptial feathers of the drake mallard (*Anas platyrhynchos*) are representative of a kind of uniform within a given species; the female is inherently attracted to a particular style and colour. Recognizing their mates is more difficult for the drakes. Females have an inconspicuous protective colouration and the plumage of one species may differ only in slight detail from the plumage of another. Therefore, the drake ducklings must learn from the example of their own mother how their future partners should look.

The degree of contrast between the white head and the iris, and the fleshy ring surrounding the iris, are the prime characteristics used by courting gulls to identify their would-be mates. The Thayer's gull (*Larus thayeri*) has a brown iris and purple-red eye ring (a), which is in greater contrast with the white head than the yellow iris and brighter yellow ring of the glaucous gull (*L. hyperboreus*) (b).

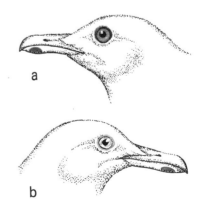

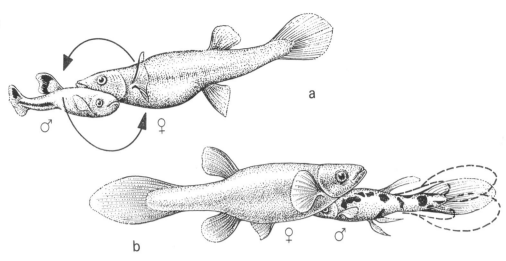

The courtship dances of the guppies *Poecilia picta* (a) and *P. reticulata* (b).

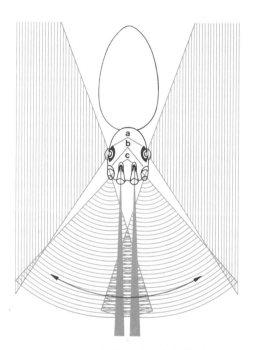

The diagram of the visual field in the jumping spiders.

dances in circles around her. When circling near her head, he spreads his dorsal and tail fins, displaying bright markings on them. In an aquarium with two related species kept together, the male may court females of either species and may even attempt to mate with both of them. However, the females prevent interbreeding by accepting love proposals only from their own males, and ignoring all attentiveness from the other ones. The cues the female uses to make the right choice are a combination of displayed colour patterns and movements which are distinct in each species. Even the male learns to distinguish subtle differences in females of different species after being rejected several times, so that the number of his 'errors' diminishes.

Jumping spiders (Salticidae) use their sight for hunting and finding their mates. The spider first detects movements of the object with its small lateral eyes (a), which have a wide vision that encompasses most of the surroundings. Then the spider swivels toward the moving object and inspects it in more detail with its large front eyes (b, c), which function as a telephoto lens, having a long focus and high visual acuity.

Jumping spiders undoubtedly are among the most beautiful of spiders. When a jumping spider on the prowl for a mate meets another spider of his species, he greets it by raising one pair of his legs. If the encountered specimen is another male, he answers with the same encounter posture and both males go on their way. If he meets a female, a wealth of visual signals will be exchanged. The female recognizes

The huge front eyes of the jumping spiders resemble the headlights of a racing car.

a male of her species by his striking colour patterns and a species-specific courtship dance the suitor performs for her. A dancing male may raise his leg or abdomen high, wave at the female, crouch or tilt, or show off a multitude of other characteristic postures or dramatic gestures while displaying striking secondary sexual attributes, such as tufts of hair and brightly pigmented scales on various parts of his body.

The choreography of courtship dances in the jumping spiders is so rich and varied that arachnologists are trying to use it for the classification within this largest spider family, having over 3,000 species described so far.

The female grants favours only to the male who proves he is the right species by performing the right courtship dance. If she has already mated, she will turn him down with a rejection gesture. In the New Zealand species *Euophrys parvula*, for instance, the female mimics the encounter posture, raising one pair of her legs as if she were another male. As we already know, in the spider's language this means 'leave me alone and be on your way'.

Wolf spiders (Lycosidae) also use visual cues during courtship, although to a lesser degree than the jumping spiders. Their eyes are capable only of registering movements, not colours. The male thus notices the female only when she moves. Similarly, the female recognizes her partner only by the species-specific movements of his body, pedipalpi and legs, while his shape and colour mean nothing to her. Since the male may court females of different species, it is up to her to prevent interbreeding. For this, she relies on her sense of hearing as well, for a courting male wolf spider also stridulates.

The courtship of fiddler crabs of the genus *Uca* is another fine example of an isolation mechanism mediated by visual cues. In his tidal shore home, the male is

The sense of touch is the most important sense used for communication in courting the largest spiders, the hairy mygalomorphs (Theraphosidae).

Males of the wolf spiders (Lycosidae) introduce themselves to their mates by waving their palpi according to a species-specific code.

The courting male of the New Zealand jumping spider *Trite auricoma* uses the vertical movements of his forelegs to introduce himself to the female.

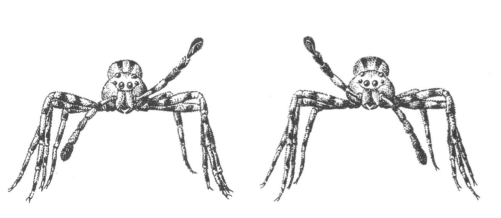

easily identified because one of his claws is several times larger than the other. The female can readily see him when he waves at her with his giant claw during courtship. When the female comes closer, his waving intensifies and is followed by vibrations of his whole body, which are also accompanied by sound effects.

Diurnal lizards such as the common iguana (*Iguana iguana*) communicate by bobbing and waving their brightly coloured heads during courtship.

Showy colour patterns are almost always displayed through special gestures or postures, which make the displaying animal even more obvious. These movements by themselves can be species specific, as in the case of lizards of the genus *Sceloporus,* as shown in the figure on the next page.

Bobbing the front part of the body is a courtship signal of common American fence lizards of the genus *Sceloporus*. Each species has a characteristic way of bobbing, differing in the number, amplitude and speed of the movements. By using an ingenious machine fixed to the head of an artificial lizard, scientists succeeded in imitating the bobbing patterns of different species, as shown on the diagram. A live female, to which the animated dummy was offered, responded positively only when the dummy bobbed in the rhythm of her own species.

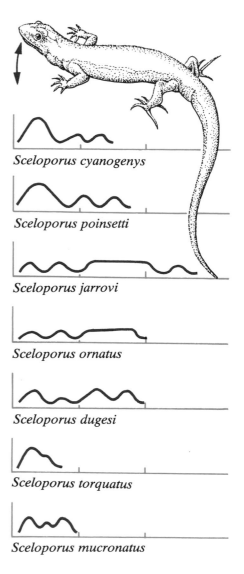

Sceloporus cyanogenys

Sceloporus poinsetti

Sceloporus jarrovi

Sceloporus ornatus

Sceloporus dugesi

Sceloporus torquatus

Sceloporus mucronatus

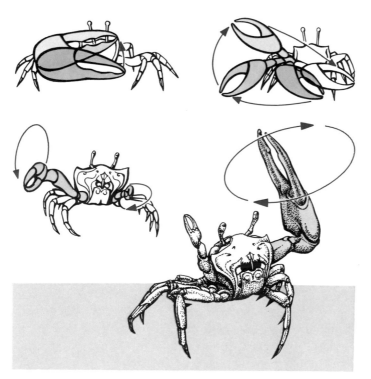

The waving display in fiddler crabs is species specific and it may vary so greatly between species that even inexperienced humans can distinguish different species, let alone the female crab. One species describes a circle, another makes various elipses, still others simply wave up and down with the claw, each species also having a distinctive frequency of movements and direction.

THE FIREFLY'S MAGIC LAMP

Luminous insects

At last we come to the most spectacular examples of optical signalization in the animal kingdom. On purpose I saved the best for last; for in nature we are also obliged to wait until the close of day, when in the twilight of a warm night, the first magic lights appear. The fragile, luminescent beetles, which inspire fairy tales and superstitions, we call fireflies.

In the common European species, *Lampyris noctiluca*, it is the female who takes the initiative in meeting the opposite sex. She is wingless and larva-like, with a huge and powerful light organ on the underside of her abdomen. The courtship takes place shortly after dusk. A female ready for mating lights up her 'lantern' and curves her candescent underbelly up above her head, as a beacon. Glowing

A copulating pair of European fireflies (*Phausis splendidula*).

constantly, she aims to be noticed by a flying male. The wooers cruise the air, and when one notices a little lantern below, he hovers directly above it long enough to take aim, then plunges at the female as a hawk would dive toward its prey.

The signal system of its North American relative, *L. reticulata,* differs slightly. The female watches for a male with her lantern off. Only when she sees him shining above her does she turn on her own light. This seemingly insignificant difference is seen by biologists studying the evolution of the communication systems of fireflies to have far reaching importance. We shall see that the female's response to the male's light challenge represents a key element in the more sophisticated flashing interactions of other American fireflies.

The females of this and related species are winged and able to fly. However, when waiting for a male, they sit on low-growing vegetation and look watchfully around with their large eyes. The males fly through the air in a seemingly chaotic fashion at different altitudes, lighting up for a moment from time to time. Each species flashes in a characteristic way. The male's flashes differ in the number, frequency and duration of light pulses, and sometimes also in the colour and intensity of light; but most important, and for each species most characteristic, are the intervals between flashes. They are the designated signal by which a female unerringly determines that the male circling above is the right one. The way she introduces herself is the simplest one that nature could have devised. In response, she flashes with a precisely timed constant delay. In the common species *Photinus pyralis,* for instance, the male flashes every six seconds, with each flash lasting half a second. The female's light response follows the male's flash after an exact two-second interval. This delay interval is a vital signal for the male, for it tells him that it is a female of his own species who is responding. The male will readily answer even the flashes of a penlight, provided the timing is exactly two seconds after his own flash.

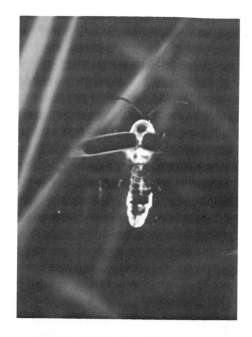

If the female firefly replies in the right interval, the flashing male will approach her while she is still respoding. In some species, the pattern of light conversation between the partners changes as they become aware of each other. The male *Photinus macdermotti,* for instance, on noticing the flashes of his female, will switch from simple flash pulses to double pulses. Simultaneously he speeds up the rate of flashing, although only by 30 milliseconds. It is not his impatience nor his excitement which causes him to do so. It is rather a precautionary measure, as we shall see later.

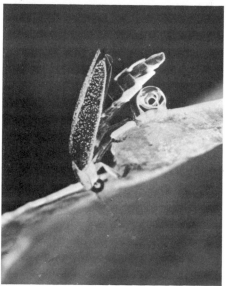

When studying flash signalling in the genus *Photinus,* Professor James E. Lloyd discovered that the females can be easily found and collected if one mimics the male's flashes with a flashlight while slowly walking through a suitable habitat. Sometimes, however, something unpredicted happened; the female which responded to his artificial signal did not belong to the genus *Photinus.* Instead, it was a large voracious female of some *Photuris* species. The premarital dialogue of the *Photuris* fireflies differs markedly from the language of smaller, *Photinus* species. Watching one such predatory female for about half an hour, the professor saw her respond 12 times to the flashes of passing *Photinus* males. Still more surprising, she responded with exactly the same delay timing as a *Photinus* female. It appeared that the *Photuris* females abuse the communicatory code of other species for purely gastronomic reasons. A strange male who allows himself to be deceived, ends up not in a passionate embrace, but fondly clamped in the

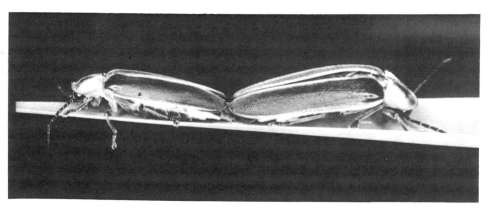

Three episodes from the sex life of the American fireflies of the genus *Photinus.* The sitting female responds to the flying male's flashes by her own coded flash signal. A few moments later the pair can be found copulating.

Each firefly species of the genus *Photinus* uses its own species-specific way of flashing.

mandibles of a hungry predator. Such imitation of someone else's signal with aggressive intentions is called aggressive mimicry. Now we can understand the precaution of the tiny male of *Photinus macdermotti*. By changing his flash code after seeing the longed-for lantern, he was making sure that the torch-bearer was indeed a female of his own species. Only she knows that she is supposed to respond by accelerating her flash responses. The predatory females have not yet learned the secret code.

An inquiring reader may wonder if the *Photuris* females are that bloodthirsty while still virgin. If yes, then how could suitors of their own species possibly avoid the fate of the seduced *Photinus* males? The essential task of a virgin female is acquiring a male to father her offspring. That is why she is at first interested only in the flashes of males of her own species, which differ greatly, as we know, from the signals of potential victims. The big change in her behaviour happens only after mating; then she is no longer the tender and meek bride, but a ravenous predator waiting greedily for her prey with mandibles wide open. Appropriately, Professor Lloyd calls the mated females *femmes fatales*. Since the period of virginity in these females lasts only a few minutes in nature, their males use a cunning trick to meet with a few more consorts. When the male is not getting any responses from females of his own species, he begins to mimick the flashes of potential prey species. If a hunting female reveals herself by her false response, the male is faced with an uneasy task: to win her favours without losing his head. He stands no chance of raping his larger and well-armed mate. For his sake, it is hoped he has some trick, unknown to us, to help persuade his hungry partner that his species identity is the acceptable one, and that he can seduce her at last. It was occasionally observed that the male switched from his false code to the one of his own species.

The communal courtship of fireflies in the tropical jungle of southeast Asia is another spectacular luminous show. Just imagine a tall tree densely covered with small, oval leaves. On each leaf sits a firefly, all flashing in perfect unison. The whole tree alternately glows and falls into complete darkness. Then picture in your mind some 150 metres of river bank densely rimmed with mangrove trees, besprinkled with countless beetles all switching their lanterns on and off in perfect agreement. This scene takes place hour after hour, night after night, for weeks or even months.

The synchronous flashing is exclusively a male activity. Since they have a life span of only a few days, whole new generations must constantly replenish the glowing trees. In the species *Pteroptyx malaccae*, thousands of males flash twice a second. Individuals never deviate from the mean flash pulse rhythm by more than 15 milliseconds. In other words, the time interval between the earliest and the latest flash is only 30 milliseconds.

The biological function of those 'light orgies' had long been a matter of speculations. Only recently was it observed that the females also participate in them, with their lanterns switched off. This finding suggested that the light festival organized by the males may serve two goals: the light calls more males from the surrounding jungle and, at the same time, it attracts virgin females to the trees. A single male would have little chance to use his lantern effectively in the dense vegetation of the tropical jungle, but the glowing trees are well visible from quite a distance, particularly along the banks of large rivers. And the synchronous flashing multiplies the attractive effect.

Female fireflies attracted by the pulsating shimmer of light will find no shortage of grooms. On the contrary, they can select from among the best. They circle around the flashing tree and reveal their presence by coquettish flashes of their own, which are out of rhythm with the male chorus. Those males that notice

The most luminous insects are the Carribean click beetles — cucujos (*Pyrophorus*). Their luminous organs are situated on the thorax and abdomen and they can emit enough light to illuminate a wristwatch.

a female will immediately start to compete for her attention. Each will turn his light organ towards her, striving to be the lucky one. The female chooses the brightest light, lands on that male's leaf, and with another flash of her lantern tells him to forget his communal flashing for the night in order to devote all his attention to her. All that follows takes place in darkness. If an observer tactfully waits a few minutes before illuminating the place of courtship with a flashlight, he can usually surprise the pair in the act of mating. It must be said that in the final phase of courtship, the couple uses scent signals to express amorous intentions.

The lanterns of fireflies are complex light emitting organs. Each is composed of three layers: an outer 'window', simply a transparent portion of the body wall; the light organ proper; and an inner layer of opaque, whitish cells filled with granules of uric acid, the so-called reflector. The light organ proper consists of elongated light cells, which are supplied with oxygen by means of numerous fine air tubes. The nerves penetrating the light organ regulate luminiscence of the lantern. It was discovered long ago that cutting off the firefly's head caused the flashing to stop. Later it was found that by electrical stimulation of the severed nerve cord one can experimentally produce flashing in the headless beetle. Quite recently it was demonstrated that small doses of insecticides cause the poisoned fireflies to glow for a long time.

The colour of the light varies in different species. Mostly it is yellowish, but it may have a greenish, bluish, or orange hue. In the luminous giant click beetles cucujos (*Pyrophorus*) there are two greenish lights just behind the head and an orange light on the abdomen. These lanterns are perhaps the strongest light organs found in the animal kingdom. The story is told that when Sir Robert Dudley and Sir James Cavendish first landed in Cuba, they saw great numbers of lights moving about in the woods. Supposing them to be Spaniards with torches ready to attack them, the British withdrew to their ships and went on to settle Jamaica. Thus cucujos may be said to have changed the course of history.

HOW MUCH CAN A FROG SAY?

Vocal communication in frogs and toads

Did it ever occur to you to ask yourself how much a frog can say, when you were listening to the serenades of those singers? The word serenade is indeed a very proper one in this context. It is the choir of males that makes that background sound of a summer evening at a swampy lake, and the songs are directed at the fair sex. But not only at them. Frogs' songs are important territorial signals, too. So, what is the true meaning of the amphibian's vocabulary?

If we tried to answer the question by ourselves, a lot of effort would be required. We would have to sneak into a crowd of chorusing frog males, pick one of them and concentrate our attention on all of his activities, watching closely and recording every movement of his body. In addition to this we would have to record and analyze all his vocal displays, play them back to other frogs and carefully watch for their responses. Certainly, one or two nights would not suffice to carry out such a study. Fortunately, such observations have already been done with professional thoroughness by several zoologists. One of them was Dr. Gary M. Fellers of the University of Maryland.

The young scientist spent more than 300 wakeful nights at a muddy pond near the village of White Oak, MD, learning the vocabulary of a North American tree frog, *Hyla versicolor*.

First, Dr. Fellers confirmed that the males of this frog species have territorial behaviour similar to that of the males of other tree frog species. Shortly after dusk, the male assumes a strategic position on the branch of a tree or shrub near water and defends this calling perch against other males. He proclaims the ownership of the perch by vocal signals known as mating calls. These consist of simple croaks which are repeated once every three to seven seconds, depending on the temperature. The owners of adjoining perches croak in turn so that one male hears the other in the break between his own calls. Voice intensity allows the male to estimate the distance of the rivals with unbelievable accuracy. As long as a neighbour's voice does not exceed a sound level of 93 dB, it does not bother him at all. In such a case, both frogs are no closer to each other than approximately 80 cm. If the neighbour or another male stranger enters his territory, the intruder's voice rises above the critical level, and the owner responds by changing his calls. His soft melodious mating calls become interspersed with a low-pitched coarse sound resembling short trains of machine-gun shots. This is the encounter call. Sometimes the challenger will slip quietly into the territory of the singer and surprise him with his encounter call from a short distance. In either case, both males will exchange several vocal threats, alternating them with the mating calls — the latter perhaps to check the distance separating them.

The European tree frog (*Hyla arborea*).

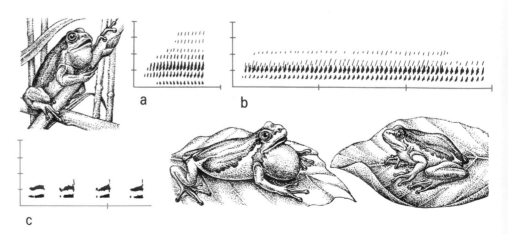

The male of the American tree frog *Hyla versicolor* delimits his territory and at the same time attracts the females with short (a) and long (b) mating calls. When trying to intimidate his rivals, he gives off a series of short shrieks (c) known as the encounter call.

50

This exchange of vocal threats is often sufficient for the intruder to leave the foreign territory. If it is not, a fight breaks out. The frogs shove each other with their forelimbs, butt with their heads, kick with their hind legs and jump on each other. No wonder one of them may fall off the perch for which they were fighting. The fight, which may last several minutes, is over when the defeated male recognizes the winner by leaving the disputed territory. But sometimes the loser takes a different tack, falling silent and remaining on the territory of the dominant male. As we shall see later, this tactic may pay off well for him. In the meantime, the winner steps up

The European tree frog lives in trees, but during the breeding season the frogs descend to ponds. From there the loud chirping can be heard every night. The sound is amplified by a resonating pouch on the male's throat.

The male green frog (*Rana esculenta*) has two resonating pouches on both sides of his head.

the broadcast of the mating calls, because now his main concern is to attract a bride.

A gravid female is attracted by the mating calls of a male from as far as several metres. She approaches him very slowly, making short jumps whenever he breaks the silence. When the female comes within a distance of about 15−25 cm from the male, he realizes her presence and welcomes her with a sound known as the long call. This is supposed to aid the orientation of the bride in her very last maiden jumps.

When the male and female finally meet, he never impatiently hugs her as is the custom of many other frog and toad species. Instead, a short nuptial ritual first takes place. The female nudges the male on the side and then turns away from him at right angles. Only then does the male turn toward her and clasps her tightly. Sometimes the female has to urge the male twice to persuade him that she is the one for him. Such a touch signal is needed mainly in habitats where several tree frog species live together. It prevents the male from paying unwanted attention to frogs of the wrong species.

Thus, in tree frogs, the nuptial clasp, or amplexus, begins on the tree. After a while, the female with the male on her back leaves the perch and moves to the water to release the eggs, which the male readily fertilizes. This is the moment for which the silent loser was so patiently waiting. He will swiftly occupy the vacant perch and while the previous owner enjoys life down in the muddy puddle, the new occupant urgently begins to call, as if to make up for lost time. Apparently, he has considered this perch worthy of waiting for rather than looking for another.

Other tree frog species display similar courtship behaviours. The most important component of their vocal repertoires again is the mating call, by which the male advertizes his location both to the neighbouring males and to the egg-laden females. To prevent misunderstanding, the mating call of one species differs distinctly from the calls of other species in at least one attribute, whether it be amplitude-frequency, amplitude or frequency modulation, number or duration of pulses or pulse repetition rate − in simple terms, each voice sounds different, at least to the frog's ear. Indeed, laboratory experiments involving synthetic male's croaks revealed that a would-be frog mother responds only to the vocal advertisement possessing certain species characteristics.

Still another call has been recognized in amphibian vocal repertoires. It commonly occurs in toads and some jumping frogs and is produced by a male on whose back another male has jumped, mistaking him for a female. The annoyed individual calls the other male's attention to the fact that he has chosen the wrong subject for his advances by making a repeated 'chuck' noise. Zoologists use the term release call when referring to this strange noise, because it literally means 'get off me'. The significance of such a call in social contacts of frogs and toads should not be underestimated. They find use for it more often than it would be expected. A love-sick male toad, paddling in the spring pudle, is not particularly choosy and grasps at everything that moves, including a large fish or a fisherman's rubber boot, when females are in short supply.

A surprising discovery made in 1964 revealed that not all courting frogs and toads are talkative. The exception proving the rule was a rare tropical species, the golden toad (*Bufo periglenes*), whose males are as shiny red as Christmas tree ornaments in the shadows of the rain forest of Montevideo. Their conspicuousness is apparently the reason why they do not have to advertize themselves vocally.

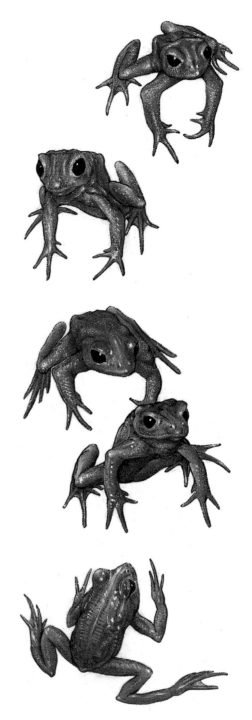

Bufo periglenes

THE COURTING OF A TUNING FORK

Acoustic courtship signals in insects

We are all familiar with that nasty sound, that ominous whine, by which a female mosquito announces her hungry presence in our lakeside tent. The chances are that we will sleepily get up to put on a light and take an angry whack at those delicate monsters. Yet, next morning our eyes open to gaze upon the one mosquito we failed to kill last night. She hangs heavily over our heads, grotesquely plump from blood sucked out of our veins. We only marvel at the ease with which we can now dispatch her. A crimson smear on the canvas taunts us until the end of vacation as a reminder of our belated bloody revenge. Had a male mosquito been in our tent while the female was preparing for her last supper, quite different thoughts would have entered his mind. The tone that to us signaled an insidious attack, could be an irresistible love call to a male mosquito.

The first scientist who seriously attempted to study this problem was the American entomologist Dr. Louis Roth, some 40 years ago. Choosing the yellow fever mosquito (*Aedes aegypti*) as an experimental object for his thesis, he soon noticed that the simplest way to make mosquitoes mate is to shake the cage and thus force them to take flight. As long as the females were on the wing, the males

The female mosquito becomes attractive to the male only after taking her first blood meal.

chased them with persistent attempts to mate. The only defence for females fed up with the males' ardour was to land; males paid no attention to sitting females, even if they accidentally touched each other in a dense crowd. Neither did freshly killed females attract the attention of wooers. It must not be smell that interests the males, reasoned the young scientist, but rather something given off by flying females. He set up experiments to find the answer.

At first he studied the effects of various sounds on the mosquitoes. Nothing seemed to excite the females. Males, however, were attracted by every tone within the frequency range of 300 to 800 Herz (Hz), whether it was a playback of the flight tone or a tone generated synthetically. After prolonged celibacy, sex-starved males could even be fooled with a tuning fork of the right pitch. They would pounce on the wall of the cage in the direction of the sound, attempting to mate with each other or with the mesh that separated them from the seductive sound. Apparently, the song of the wings was what both the student and the male mosquitoes were chasing.

Even in the short life of the female mosquito, there are periods when she has no interest in sex, and when in fact any attention from the male would annoy her. This may be the time when she looks for a warm-blooded animal to supply nutrients for her first batch of eggs. Indeed a young, hungry female can manage to save her virginity even in a cage full of grown males, because the tone she produces in flight is out of the range of frequencies that stimulate the sexual drive in males.

It was not difficult to discover the organs of hearing in the males. The most conspicuous organs that distinguish the sexes are the antennae. In males they are larger and more plumated than those of the females. When Roth cut off both antennae of a male, the poor insect became deaf. The same effect was observed when the antennae were immobilized by a coating of shellac applied to their base. The males ceased to respond to females even when only the tips of their antennae were weighted with a small drop of lacquer. When the weight was removed, they resumed sensitivity to the love song of the female. Finally, merely shaving off the plumage of the antennae made the males hard of hearing; they ignored their mates, but the considerably louder sound of a tuning fork still made them excited. From these and from other observations, Louis Roth concluded that the plumose flagellum (that is, the feather-like part of the antenna) picks up faint vibrations of the air caused by sound waves. Movements of the flagellum are registered by the mechanoreceptors of the so called Johnston's organ located in the base of each antenna.

The 'song of the wing' also serves as the main courtship signal in the 'short-horned' flies, evolutionarily more advanced relatives of the mosquitoes. However, these advanced flies have considerably improved their vocal pre-marital conversation. They no longer use the acoustic signal that arises as a mere by-product of the flight movement of the wings, but they actively and purposefully create their love songs. Fruitflies (Drosophilidae) are the true masters of this art. These tiny red fruitflies are the ones that appear as if by magic in the kitchen when one leaves an unfinished glass of wine or a bowl of well-ripened fruit uncovered.

The fruitfly is probably the most commonly used laboratory insect, with an invaluable merit for the advancement of genetics. It was predestined for this task by the fact that the female becomes a grandmother in a couple of weeks and does not keep an impatient scientist waiting long for the results of crossbreeding. Life in a test tube does not give much opportunity for keeping one's intimacy a secret: that is why we know more about the mating of fruitflies than we have learned about the physiology of love-making in our own species.

The courting male approaches the female from a distance of some two millimetres, extending his right wing as an instrument for making the characteristic

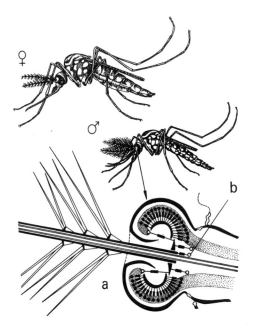

The male mosquito has more plumated antennae than the female. The movements of his antenna caused by the sound waves are registered by the Johnston's sensory organ (a) located in the antenna's spherical basal segment, which is loaded with mechanoreceptors (b).

This tiny male of the midge family, pictured on my daughter's finger copulating, hears through his plumated antennae (arrow).

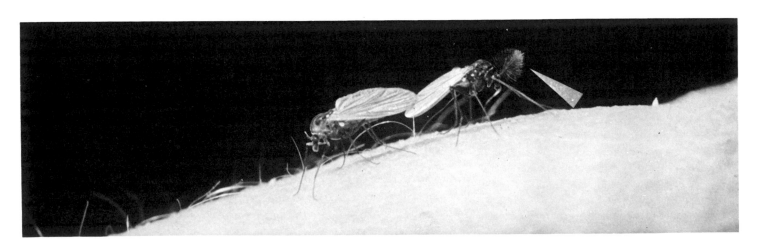

The antennae (a) are the organs of hearing also in the fruitflies. If two males (b) simultaneously court one female (c), the one standing face to face toward her has a better chance of being accepted, because his song sounds 15 dB louder at her antennae than the song of his rival who courts the female from behind.

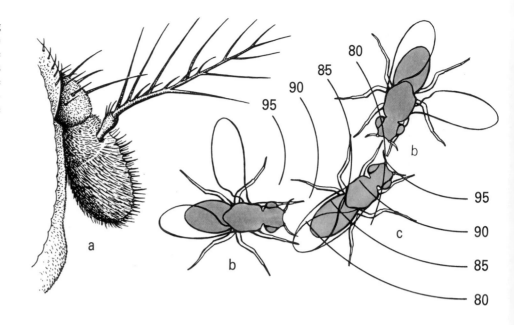

One decibel (dB) is a unit for measuring the relative loudness of sounds equal to the smallest degree of difference of loudness ordinarily detectable by the human ear on a scale beginning with 1 for the faintest audible sound and ending with 130 for the loudest distinguishable sound intensity.

sounds. If she wants to turn him down, she responds with a short buzz at a frequency of about 300 Hz. The male is not usually discouraged by her first refusal and persists in his courtship song. Very often the female gives herself up only after a prolonged insistent serenade. If, however, she is not in the mood for mating (if she is, for example, sexually immature or already fertilized), or if it is a male of a different species who courts her, then the male's intimacies truly annoy her; she gives him a kick and takes off. The comparison of mating songs of different fruitflies reveals that, whereas the rejection signal of the female is basically the same in all species (perhaps because it is meant to be understood by the males of all species), the courtship song of the male is always strictly species specific.

One can hardly believe that laboratory recordings sounding like the troubled engine of a model airplane or the cackling of a startled hen are produced by an instrument as delicate as the wing of a fruitfly. Only a thorough acoustic analysis can clarify this paradox.

One of the simplest fruitfly songs appears to be that of *Drosophila melanogaster*. The male waves his wing about thirty times a second, which roughly corresponds to the vibration frequency of the lowest piano string. But the tiny singer is by no means a murmurer. His voice sounds rather like the piercing whirr of a motorcycle engine without its silencer. Indeed, the oscilloscope image of the sound is far from being a perfect sinusoid curve, such as that of the tone of the piano string. Instead, it is a series of short pulses, each lasting for a mere six thousandth of a second (msec). The pulses are regularly repeated once in 34 msec for a total of 30 beats per second. Each pulse is produced by an incredibly fast movement of the wing followed by a relatively long (28 msec) period, during which the wing is completely at rest. Knowing the area of the wing and the amplitude of its movement, an acoustician can easily assess the usefulness of the characteristics of that odd sound for communication between the tiny flies.

What comes as the biggest surprise is its loudness in close proximity to the singer. When the male politely circles the chosen mate, only half his body length away from her forehead, his voice reaches her ears at a sound level of 95 decibels, a level corresponding to the roar of a loud car horn. Thus the love dialogue of the fruitflies, in terms of their own microworld, is several hundred times louder than a normal conversation among people.

Out of the 22 fruitfly species acoustically studied, the courtship song of only six was found to be composed of simple pulses similar to those of the song of *D. melanogaster*. What characterizes all the songs is the length of the intervals between the pulses. Perhaps this is the acoustic parameter that serves as the identification signal for a given species and which represents the isolation mechanism preventing cross-matings between the species. An experiment was promptly designed to test this page. Instead of simple pulses (e.g. *D. bipectinata*), their songs are composed of and subsequently released them into a cage with 50 virgin females of the same species. Only a few males succeeded in mating during a 12-minute test. Apparently the wing stumps of the crippled males were unable to produce enough noise to excite females and to make them ready for copulation. When, however, an artificially produced pulsed sound was simultaneously played back to the reluctant lovers, the number of mating pairs increased significantly, although the miracle happened only when the 'wedding march' had the pulse interval of exactly the required 34 milliseconds!

Courtship songs of many other fruitfly species appeared more complicated than that of the common *Drosophila*, as illustrated in the oscillograms at the bottom of this page. Instead of simple pulses (e.g. *D. bipectinata*), their songs are composed of pulse trains of variable length and frequency (e. g. *D. persimilis*). In an extreme case the intervals of silence are completely absent (e. g. *D. athabasca*) so that the wing produces a continuous buzz. The buzz, however, differs from the monotonous hum of mosquito wings in having its species characteristic melody. New tunes thus can be added to the fruitfly song-book, each representing a behavioural fingerprint of a species. These tiny flies surely need them: the genus *Drosophila* alone may contain as many as 2,000 species, all closely resembling each other both in appearance and way of life, and there hardly exists a region in the world where several species are not found together.

Grasshoppers, locusts, katydids, crickets and mole crickets — in short Orthopterans — can rightly be called the vocal elite among the insects. It is their songs that

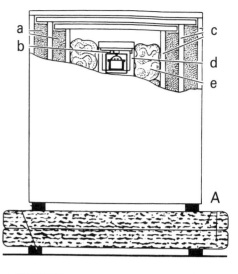

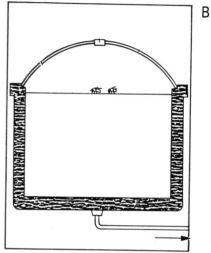

It is not easy to record the fruitfly songs, because of their extremely low volume. In terms of power output, the signal given off by the male wing does not exceed a ten-billionth of watt. Just for comparison, the speakers of modern radio receivers have an output a billion times higher! That is why scientists have to install a supersensitive microphone into an elaborate sound-proof box (A) and allow the tested flies to mate directly on the membrane of the microphone (B). Even under these circumstances, it was advantageous to record late at night or during weekends, when the laboratory was completely silent. (a – sand; b – light; c – plasterboard boxes; d – lead cylinder; e – insulating material.)

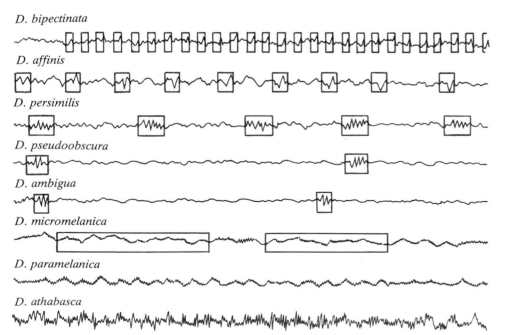

D. bipectinata

D. affinis

D. persimilis

D. pseudoobscura

D. ambigua

D. micromelanica

D. paramelanica

D. athabasca

Song oscillograms of various species of fruitflies of the genus *Drosophila*.

make the heavy rhythms that hang in the summer air and are inseparable from the whole season's scenario. One can easily pick out different species by their voices, but the messages coded in their songs can be understood only with the aid of sophisticated acoustic analyzers. Voice is the principal means of communication among members of their own species for the majority of Orthopterans. Realizing that there may be about 15 thousand species in the world, that each species may have a repertoire of several songs, and that hardly any two species share identical songs, we must conclude that their 'song-book' is unparalleled in the animal · kingdom.

Orthopterans make use of their musical instruments mainly for courtship. The sound produced by the male for calling a mate is known as the proclamation song. The male field cricket (*Gryllus campestris*) sings at the entrance to its burrow. A receptive female responds to his song from as far away as 10 metres. She approaches haltingly, stopping to correct the course of her march. A blinded female would behave the same way as a sighted one, likewise a female which is upwind will respond no different than one which is downwind. This is because neither sight nor smell guide her during her quest for a mate.

In 1913 a German zoologist, J. Regen, performed his now famous experiment with a pair of crickets and a telephone. He demonstrated that the female is attracted by the male's voice even if it is transmitted by an apparatus. The male's voice lost its highest pitched tones due to imperfections in the transmission, yet the female responded assuredly, as if the male were standing in the same room with her. This is because the rhythm of the song was not altered by the phone transmitter. An expert would say that the high frequency tones of the stridulating insect carry the specific low frequency modulatin embodying the message, according to which the female distinguishes a calling partner of her own species. The illustration on page 60 makes it more obvious.

Now that we understand the principles of the cricket's stridulation, let us have a look at what is behind the one-of-a-kind nature of different species' songs. What characteristics make up the variables? The first one to consider is the basic frequency of the wing membrane. The length of the pulse is another possibility; it is determined by the length of the 'bow' and by the speed of its movements. The number of pulses in each chirp can vary as can the inter-pulse pause. Finally, the time interval between the chirps can differ in different species. All of these variables in combination create almost infinite possibilites.

Based on numerous experiments, a conclusion was made that the melody of the song says nothing to the cricket's ear. It is the rhythm that is all-important for species discrimination. The basic carrying frequency could only be significant if the organs of hearing in individual species were finely tuned to the frequencies of their own songs, which would prevent them from hearing the songs of other species. Such a specialization for a narrow frequency band has indeed been proven to occur in a few rare cases. Small ground crickets (Nemobiinae), which often live together with large field crickets, sing one or two octaves higher than their more prodigious cousins.

Frogs, fruitflies and crickets and their kin all use the same solution to the problem of cohabiting with related species in a common biotope: they sing a song which differs from that of their related neighbours. The males of two different species can use the same signal only when their habitats do not overlap. This is the case for the

The terror of African tropics,
the desert locust (*Schistocerca gregaria*).

58

The organs of hearing in crickets and grasshoppers are on the tibia, just beneath the knee. The white eardrum of the singing male cricket *Gryllus bimaculatus* can be seen as a white spot on his front leg.

The diagram at the bottom of p. 61 shows how scientists investigated the behaviour of the vocal hybrids between two cricket species of the genus *Teleogryllus*. Walking along a featherweight styrofoam Y-maze, a tethered female listens to different hybrid males' calling songs played simultaneously by equidistant speakers. She reveals her preference at the fork of the maze by walking in the direction of one of the speakers. (Hybrid songs: a − *T. oceanicus* ♀ × *T. commodus* ♂; b − *T. commodus* ♀ × *T. oceanicus* ♂.)

The stridulation of crickets is done by rubbing the front wings together (a). Each wing is equipped with a file (red) and scraper (blue) for this purpose (b). As the wings move, the teeth of the file strike the sharp scraper, which makes a sound similar to that of a bow moving across a violin string. The tone is amplified by a special resonating area on the wing membrane. With each movement of the 'bow', a pulse of pure, high-pitched tone arises. A group of several pulses form the syllable (c) − let us call it a chirp. The whole cricket's song is composed of a series of chirps (d).

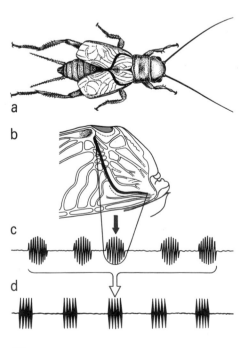

European field cricket (*Gryllus campestris*), which has one vocal double in the Bermudas (*G. bermudiensis*), another in the North American continent (*G. firmus*), and possibly others might be found when more is learned about crickets in other parts of the world. When such related cricket species with identical stridulation are put together in a laboratory, they interbreed without problem. It is quite another matter to persuade representatives of two different species to mate if their courtship songs do not match. When such a mating is successful, the song of the sons is a blend of the songs of the parent species. In Nature, such a vocal bastard would have a slim chance of finding a mate. His sisters would not be any better off, being unable to understand the songs of normal males. This has been demonstrated by an experiment which is illustrated in a diagram at the bottom of this page.

Mole crickets are close relatives of the field crickets. Among the group of orthopterans, they hold several records. Being five centimetres long and weighing several grams, they are the heftiest members of the order, at least in the temperate region. More interesting than his size is another trait of the vineyard mole cricket male (*Gryllotalpa vinae*): he produces the loudest and purest sound in the insect world. The male starts calling shortly after sunset, at first haltingly and with diffidence. When fully wound up, however, his voice takes on the bold tintinnabulation of an electric doorbell. His loud and plain monotonous song rings for an hour or more without interruption. On a quiet evening, one can hear it from a distance of 600 metres, yet he sings inside his burrow.

The mole cricket's song burrow is a standardized shape, having the parameters of what acousticians call the exponential sound-wave guide. To put it simply, it resembles the megaphone of an auctioneer. Such a sound-wave guide has the optimum properties for transmitting acoustic energy. It seems that mole crickets were ahead of our acoustic engineers by several million years.

The mole cricket is apparently the only animal that consciously, though

60

A portrait of one of the best insect singers, the mole cricket (*Gryllotalpa gryllotalpa*).

The burrow of a male mole cricket, *Gryllotalpa vinae,* constructed in the form of a double horn acts in a manner analogous to a loudspeaker. Songs sung outside the burrow have only about 4 per cent as much acoustic power as those sung inside the burrow.

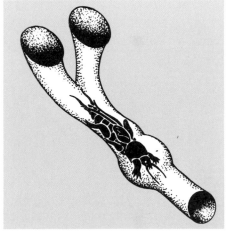

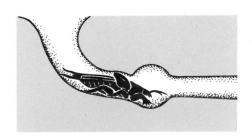

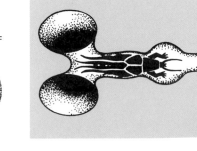

instinctively, changes its environment for acoustic reasons. The sound pressure level one metre from the burrow entrance is 90 dB and at the mouth of the burrow is a resounding 115 dB! How could virgin mole cricket females fail to be enthralled by the male's stentorous megaphone, as they fly near the ground at dusk?

Beside the fine solos of the field and mole crickets, the serenades of other orthopterans such as grasshoppers and locusts may seem like the performance of a drunk's caterwaul. This is because their musical instruments are less than perfect. Grasshoppers and katydids stridulate just as crickets do, by rubbing the file and scraper of their forewings together. However, the resonating fields of their wings are damped by the rest of their wing, so that the sound produced lacks the purity of the crickets' song. The stridulation of the locusts and the short-horned grasshoppers contains even more rasping and grating notes. That is because their song is created by rubbing the inner toothed edge of their hind legs against a fortified vein in their forewings, which have no special resonating field at all. Despite these musical imperfections, the courtship of some of the locusts serves as a nice example of an elaborate insect love dialogue.

The male prairie locust leaps from one place to another with long jumps. Upon

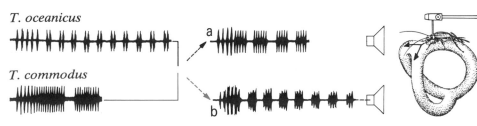

T. oceanicus

T. commodus

landing, he loudly calls for the female. If one is in the vicinity, she chirps a reply. The male counters by turning toward her sound, ardently calling again. They continue their responses as if to make sure they do not lose one another. It is surprising how easily one can provoke lonely male prairie locusts into having a dialogue with a loudspeaker in a laboratory, which plays back the female's song. The confused males excitedly hop around the elusive source of the female's call, and some even jump on the loudspeaker. This is a strong evidence that all that male and female need to find each other are the right sound signals.

When the partners have found each other, the dialogue usually continues in a more intimate key. Now the male not only courts the female with musical variations, but also caresses her gently with his antennae and displays his hind wings, which are often brightly coloured. During this phase, acoustic stimulation is thus complemented with touch, sight and smell.

The act of mating in locusts may not mean the end of the male's concern for and dialogue with the female. Some males may celebrate having scored with a partner by loud triumph calls. Similar post-copulatory calls are known to be made by satisfied male crickets. This call is supposed to mollify the female and to prevent her from prematurely removing the spermatophore which the male has deposited in her vagina during copulation; it takes time for the spermatozoids to move from the spermatophore into the female's spermatheca. The song the male sings is also meant to talk her out of possibly leaving him. Her faithfulness is also solicited by tenderly touching her antennae. Males show the opposite extreme of behaviour toward other males, chasing away all intruders by using aggressive calls known as the rivalry song.

In contrast to songsters with a large vocal repertoire, the only type of song a long-legged Central American cricket, *Amphiacusta maya,* is able to produce is a rivalry song. These crickets, unlike other known cricket species, engage in group

Courtship in a grasshopper, *Paracinema tricolor,* as well as in other short-horned grasshoppers, is accompanied by soft stridulation of both sexes.

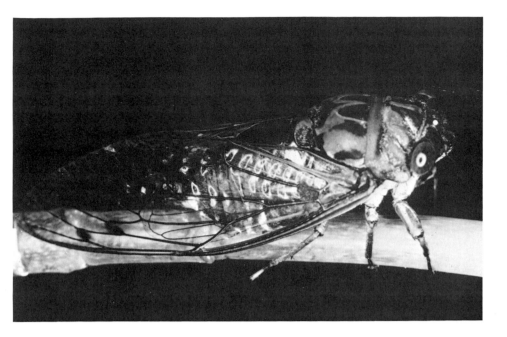

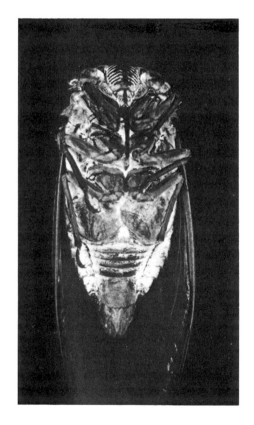

The American cicada of the genus *Magicicada*. The males have two large stridulatory organs on the ventral side of their abdomens (below). These cicadas appear regularly in large quantities only once in 13 or 17 years.

sex, a beahviour associated with their gregarious life. Groups of adults of both sexes and immature nymphs gather, usually in hollow trees, at dusk. The only thing one can hear is the loud chirping that emanates from the holes, accompanied by skirmishes among the males. The song of the male in this species is no love song, but rather war propaganda, meant to warn and intimidate other males who might dare to interfere with his silent courtship.

If cicadas were listed along with crickets as singing stars on a marquee, they would certainly receive equal billing. This is perhaps because their musical instruments are among the most efficient nature has ever evolved. In cicadas, these sound generating organs are the sole property of the males and are to be found on the ventral side of the abdomen. The principal parts of the instrument are two circular drums, called the tymbal organs, which are reinforced along their perimeters. When at rest, the drum membrane is convex. Under the middle of it is attached a bundle of muscles. When the muscles contract, the membrane produces a clicking noise, similar to that produced by a tin lid on a fruit jar when it is depressed. When these muscles are contracting 400 times per second, a fairly loud chirping results. Male cicadas have several songs in their repertoire. The one so well known that it symbolizes a scorching summer day is their chorusing song, with which they call each other to particular trees. This tree then serves as a sound beacon for attracting females. The song also functions as a territorial signal by encouraging the males to space themselves out neighbourly on the tree. Each singer synchronizes his calling with other members of the chorus, which results in a deafening noise. Even 20 m away the noise level is maintained at 80 dB.

What female cicada could resist such a rush on her sensations? When she selects a particular singer and lands nearby, her future partner falls silent, as if in fear of frightening her away. After a few moments, he starts up a softer courtship call, which may have at least three variations. The male continues to sing up until he achieves genital connection with the female. If the male makes a blunder and courts another male, the annoyed chorister rejects him with a spluttering sound.

There are many other insects that have an equally impressive musical repertoire, but their noises are far less conspicuous. Sound is also a good means of communication in water. The stridulation of the predatory water boatmen *Sigara striata* (Corixidae) was described by an entomologist, R. Ball, as early as 1846. Later investigators spent much time listening to the creaking and squeaking of other water bugs in experimental tanks. An analysis of the bugs' sounds revealed a lot of interesting details. It appears that both sexes stridulate, but the male's song is more emphatic and varied. It is used mainly as a combative signal in territorial disputes with neighbours and rivals. Males of all species of water boatmen understand this signal. However, the male's courtship song is understood only by a receptive female of the singer's species. When she hears the serenade, she stops for a moment and then answers in a low tone. Her reply is called the agreement signal. Only after getting this go-ahead response can the male approach her and try to copulate.

Water striders (Gerridae) have similar nuptial habits, with their own personal touch. Even though they can fly, they spend most of their lives skating on the water surface, thanks to the waterproof hairs on their tarsi. They feed mainly on insects that fall onto the water surface and get water-logged. The drowning insect's struggles produce waves on the water surface which function as a dinner bell for the striders. During the mating season, however, the bugs pay more attention to signals other than those produced by their prey. They begin to produce their own surface waves by making vertical oscillations with their legs, which are the main courtship signal.

The stoneflies (Plecoptera) also use a percussive approach to courtship, drumming on the leaves on which they rest. Just for this purpose, they have a special hammer on the ventral surface of their abdomens. The staccato sound has a species-specific rhythm. The male initiates the call and only a virgin female responds. In some species, the partners have to exchange the signals as many as four times before they feel confident that they are a match. In others, the female joins the male in his 'drum serenade', and only a successful duet confirms that they belong to the same species. If an impatient male mistakenly grabs another male, the latter gives a release call; he does not pound on the leaf but makes a sound by vibrating his abdomen in the air.

The tom-tom method of communication is mastered by the wood worms. The well-known 'death-watch' tacking sound is produced by the male of *Anobium striatum*. When he is obsessed with love, he beats his body against the wall of his wooden gallery.

The list of inventive insects is far from exhausted by these few examples. Some six-legged lovers are known to hiss their courtship signals to each other. The giant Madagascarian cockroach *Gomphadorhina portentosa* is familiar among hobbyists for the audible hisses it makes when touched. The ominous sound comes from a pair of abdominal tracheal spiracles, which lost their respiratory function during evolution. It was discovered only recently that in these fearsome giant cockroaches a hissing of different acoustic parameters serves as a courtship and mating signal. Experimentally muted males are unable to copulate, even if their behaviour seems quite normal.

The insects breathe by means of tracheae, which are internal tubes conducting air from the exterior through openings called spiracles to the cells of the body. The tracheae are segmentally arranged and branch repeatedly among the organs.

Kishinev, Moldavia, August 1978. One of my colleagues, Dr. Václav Skuhravý, was giving a talk at a symposium devoted to new approaches to insect pest control. Reporting on the latest results of his study of sex attractants of the lymantriid moths, he showed slides of sticky traps containing hundreds of males outsmarted by man. He presented data on the occurence, distribution and migrations of those much-feared pests, data that could only be obtained because of the unbelievable sensitivity of the males to the scent of sexually aroused females. Enthusiastically the entomologist also described the course and results of field experiments which he performed in South Bohemia only a few days previously.

Suddenly, from nowhere, a moth fluttered by the speaker, and, in no time, another one appeared. They both began circling around the man, sometimes

HOW TO WOO WITH FRAGRANCE

Sex pheromones in moths

One of the most sensitive organs of smell in the animal kingdom is the antenna of the male gypsy moth (*Porthetria dispar*).

65

Pheromones are chemical substances that affect the behaviour of other individuals of the same species. They are the means of intraspecific chemical communication.

looping farther away but then again mobbing him with even more persistence. Experts in the auditorium quickly identified them as males of a serious pest, the gypsy moth (*Porthetria dispar*). I must confess that at first it occured to me, and apparently not only to me, that somebody from the Czechoslovak delegation released at the right moment the poor moths so that they would find their way to the speaker, who most certainly had a bit of attractant somewhere in his pocket. I appreciated this as a good practical joke to revive the attention of the audience. But I was completely wrong.

The speaker needed no attractant dispenser nor a co-conspirator with the live males. An imperceptible amount of the synthetically prepared sexual lure that had remained on his hands since the experiments in the South Bohemian forests was sufficient for confusing the Moldavian gypsy moths. Males from a nearby park must have smelled the presence of the perfumed entomologist and followed the scent trail all the way through an open window right to the lecture hall. The fact that the breeze brought a few molecules of the scent to their antennae at the time of his lecture is a coincidence which we would talk about for a good many years. This event became the most eloquent demonstration of the fantastic activity of disparlure, one of the first insect sex pheromones to be identified and prepared synthetically by man.

The mystical attraction of virgin female moths has been known to entomologists for a long time. Since the last century insect collectors have been using imprisoned females to lure male specimens of rare moths. By this method they often obtained species previously unknown in the region.

The female meal moth (*Ephestia kuehniella*) attracts the males with a pheromone which is released from the glands located on her extended ovipositor.

An unfertilized female behaves in a specific way. The gypsy moth, for instance, elevates the tip of her abdomen and rhythmically extends and withdraws its last two telescopic segments. With this motion, she facilitates the secretion of a pheromone from the glands located between them. She does this only at a particular time of day. At the same time, independently, the males become possessed by restlessness and desire. The pheromone which the female releases cannot be detected by the

human nose. The moth male is, however, aroused by a few scant molecules of the compound brought to him in a breeze as a message from the female.

He takes off, and, flying against the wind, he follows the scent trail up to the source. Should he lose the scent, he stops the upwind flight and makes every effort to find it again with broad zig-zag excursions in all directions. He is so obssessed by the scent itself that he does not care about the sight of the female at all. An unfertilized female shut inside a matchbox will attract males from a wide area with the same effectiveness as would the same female in a wire cage. A cotton ball left for some time in a vial with a live female and then put in storage will attract males even after a period of several years. Not only can males find the cotton ball from a great distance, but when they draw near to it, they will even court it. Charmed by its smell, they perform a typical nuptial dance around the ball as if it were a most attractive bride. If the male moth were offered a real female encased in an air-tight glass bottle, he would show disdain toward her, despite being divided by only the thinnest of transparent barriers.

Isolation and chemical identification of the first insect pheromone was reported in 1959. The pheromone in question was that of the silkworm (*Bombyx mori*). Obtaining a mere 12 mg of the compound in highly purified state had taken a research team of Bavarian biochemists, led by the Nobelist Dr. Adolf Butenandt, some twenty years of persistent work. Half a million silkworm females paid for this tiny drop of magic liquid with their lives. They all became involuntary donors of the scent glands from the tip of their abdomen. The sex pheromone was identified as an unsaturated 16 carbon alcohol, E10, Z12-hexadecadienol, and given the name bombykol after the scientific name of its producer.

During the quarter of a century that has lapsed since then, pheromones of more than five hundred moth species have been identified. The number does not appear so impressive when one considers that there are over 100,000 species of lepidopterans living on Earth. In the early days of pheromone research, when only bombykol and a few other insect pheromones were known, some scientists believed that each species would produce a different compound as its pheromone. This view, however, had to be radically revised as the data on pheromone composition in other species amassed. Advanced micro-analytical methods revealed that the pheromones are rather complex blends of two or often many more components, usually with one compound prevailing; the compound detected by the early, less sensitive methods was only the major component.

The existence of multicomponent sex pheromones is well justified by their biological function. We should keep in mind they serve as communication between sexes, helping insects to find and distinguish the right mate. Blends of compounds are much better suited than a single chemical for this job. After all, Nature would hardly find enough chemicals of suitable physical-chemical properties for all the myriad species that need them. But blending two, three or more suitable compounds in various proportions makes it possible for a limited number of chemicals to make practically unlimited numbers of combinations. The only limiting factor then becomes the acuity of the 'nose' to which the blend is destined.

Not all components of the complex sex pheromones necessarily act as a lure. The female love scent has still other functions in the sex life of moths. When the male finally reaches his scented target, only then do the minor components come into use, as if they were more intimate sentences in the chemical dialogue of love. As the odour intensifies in close proximity to the female, the pheromone ceases its function as a driving stimulus for the foolish flight of a wooer along the volatile plume of molecules. The flight mood leaves him and a high concentration of the

Data on the distances from which the males of some moths can smell the female are startling. Large saturniids were shown to find their calling mates after being released several miles downwind from them.

The sex attractant of the unfertilized female of the lesser emperor moth (*Saturnia pavonia*) is emitted from the glands on her telescopically extended ovipositor.

pheromone impels him to search in the vicinity for the luring female, often aided by his sight, hearing and other senses. The male is perhaps stimulated to do all this by those minor components of the pheromone blend which he could not perceive from a long distance. The scent message of the female is, in fact, a rather complex chemical sentence composed of several chemical words. Each of them has a different meaning, but all contribute to achieving the final goal. The message may, for instance, be: 'Come on, sit down and make love to me!' Only three chemical words are needed – come, sit, love. Ethologists would call them attractant, arrestant and aphrodisiac.

So far we have been dealing only with the pheromones of female moths. It is time to say that many males have also their fragrant magic. On various places of the body, e. g. on the tip of the abdomen or at the base of the wings, they have pouches connected with the outlet of scent glands. These are called androconia. A sexually aroused male extrudes from them tufts of hairs, so called 'hair pencils', soaked with the scent. They facilitate the dispersal of the male pheromone. The male usually dances a circle around the female, fanning his wings to direct the fragrance toward her. The pheromone is assumed to have mainly aphrodisiacal effects on the female. It is a compound by which the six-legged groom introduces himself to the bride, woos and seduces her. It assures the calling female that a wooer of her own species had arrived and gives a shortcut to an otherwise lengthy courtship. A receptive female responds readily to the fragrance by assuming a provocative posture, which leaves the male in no doubt about her total agreement. The use of the word 'fragrance' is fully justified in the case of male pheromones, because these scents are truly aromatic even to the human nose, smelling for example of almond or chocolate.

Males of some butterflies have particularly well-developed androconia. In this group of diurnal lepidopterans, the male does not seek the female by his sense of

The tortricid moth males attracted and excited by the female's pheromone dance vigorously around her while fluttering their wings and offering their own sex pheromone. The male pea moth (*Cydia nigricana*), deceived with a synthetic lure, performs his nuptial dance on the roof of a pheromone trap.

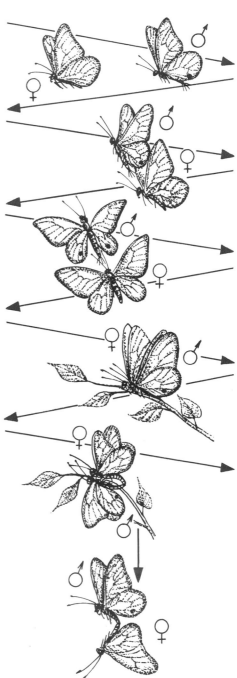

A mating pair of the butterfly *Melitaea aurelia.*

smell, but rather by sight. He chases her on the wing, first circling around and then persuading her to land. He does so again by the language of scent; he extrudes fragrant hair pencils from the tip of his abdomen and flies just ahead of her so that he brushes her antennae with them until she yields and lands. Even then, the male still flutters for a while above her, touching her antennae with his fragrant fan to make sure that she does not take off when he lands to make more intimate approaches.

Several years ago, a group led by Professor H. H. Shorey of the University of California, Riverside, reported the discovery of another surprising function of the male pheromone in the noctuid moth *Pseudaletia unipunctata.* The aromatic compound given off by a courting male, strange to say, affects mainly the other males. The pheromone simply suppresses their response to the lure of the courted female. The unpleasant consequences of the temporary 'impotence' of the other males can be beneficial to the species for it saves them wasting time waiting, and they immediately fly away to find another virgin female.

Among moths, there are species in whom the sex attractant is given off by the male. The best known example is the lesser wax moth (*Achroia grisella*), a pest who feeds on honey-combs. While looking for the male, females do not rely only on their sense of smell. The sharp smell of aldehydes composing the male pheromone does not attract them directly. Instead, it stimulates them to search for the producer of the smell, guided by their sense of hearing. A deafened female runs about excitedly for a long time before she finds the male, whereas a female deprived of her sense of smell finds him easily if placed within a hearing distance of him.

A behavioural sequence typical of the courtship of some butterflies as exemplified by the queen butterfly (*Danaus gilippus*). Note that the male offers the female the pheromone from the hair pencils on the tip of his abdomen, while still on the wing.

There are many types of pheromone traps for monitoring the flight of insect pests. Males of the notorious defoliator of coniferous trees, the larch bud moth (*Zeiraphera diniana*), can be conveniently caught in traps made of a paper cup smeared inside with a glue. A synthetic pheromone evaporates from a rubber stopper, seen in the upper part of the trap.

Mating of all moths has a species-specific time schedule. The female calls only at a particular time of day, and only at that time is the male responsive to her. As we have seen, the gypsy moth is a typical daytime lover. Many other species, such as, for instance, the hawk-moths, take advantage of the shelter of dusk when the air is still warm enough for their flight. The remainder of the night is divided, for love-making, among various nocturnal species which are usually protected against the night chill by furry coats. The timing of their nuptial flights may be so accurate that two sympatric species can use the same pheromone at the same location without danger of hybridization provided the periods of their flights do not overlap.

An ethologist who is loathe to rise early should not take up the study of insects whose love-making time is at dawn. I know that from my own experience. For two seasons, I set the alarm clock night after night for 3 a.m. in order to convince myself of the punctuality of the male moths of two different species in keeping their dates with the females. One of them was the biggest North American saturniid, the cecropia moth (*Hyalophora cecropia*), with a wingspan of 160 mm. The other was one of the smallest European tortricids, *Cnephasia pumicana*, a wheat pest with a wingspan of barely 10 mm. The arrival of the first male giant as well as of the first male dwarf to the cage containing a virgin female could have been predicted with remarkable accuracy to within five minutes.

The interest of scientists in insect sex pheromones has a sound practical reason. The pheromones have been considered as a potential tool in insect pest control programmes ever since their fantastic biological activity was recognized. The classic control methods based on toxic insecticides have several drawbacks. Besides the target pests, the insecticides hit also many beneficial species. The pest insects, in turn, develop resistant strains in response to the prolonged use of pesticides, and, consequently, increasingly higher doses of the chemicals are needed to achieve the same effect. Moreover, the toxic residues are known to accumulate in nature endangering all living organisms including man. This all calls for a considerate use of the toxicants; they should be applied only as the last resort and in the smallest possible amounts. To achieve this goal, insect sex attractants may be helpful in different ways.

The traps baited with synthetic pheromones have been used for detection of various lepidopteran pests or for monitoring seasonal fluctuations in their occurrence. The data thus obtained are particularly useful for the determination of the right time for insecticide treatment. In the simplest case, the spraying is done when the numbers of males captured in the monitoring traps reach a certain critical level. Such monitoring traps have been available for the codling moth (*Cydia pomonella*) and several other orchard pests for many years.

Synthetic sex attractants may get an opportunity to assist man in suppressing the insect pest populations in yet another way. The entomologists are investigating ways of trapping enough males to make the females short of mates. Encouraging results have been reported from the entomologists who are engaged in the control of the stored food pests.

Perhaps the most sophisticated method based on synthetic sex lures was suggested by the pioneers of pheromone research as early as the 1960s, when the only identified insect pheromone was bombykol. The scientists realized that a few milligrams of the synthetic compound represented the magic attractiveness of half a million of silkworm females. Such an army of troops transformed into a small

Dr. Hans Hummel uses caged virgin females to lure cecropia moth males (*Hyalophora cecropia*) for his investigations.

drop of oily liquid could perhaps be cleverly used against the males, reasoned the scientists. How about distributing the perfume over the fields or forests to confuse the males possessed by the desire to mate? This hide-and-seek game with the omnipresent female would be bound to frustrate and exhaust even the most persistent suitor.

The first field trial of this male confusion method was performed in 1967. The target was the cabbage looper (*Trichoplusia ni*). The results were encouraging. Since then the money spent on large-scale tests against dozens of agricultural and forest pests can be counted in millions of dollars. However, the research was commercially successful in only one case, that of the cotton ball worm (*Pectinophora gossipiella*). Since the late 1970s, environmentally concerned growers can use, as an alternative to toxic insecticides, a preparation called gossyplure, which is a synthetic pheromone worked into plastic hollow fibres. The fibres are disseminated by hundreds of thousands over the cotton-fields and the pheromone slowly evaporates from them. The treatment reportedly enables a decrease of 80 per cent to be made in the use of insecticides. Another benefit is that the pheromone treatment is harmless to the parasites and predators, who can thus significantly contribute to the control of the pest populations weakened by the confusant.

71

MATING

A comparison of the courtships in different animal species reveals a feature common to all of them. Their behaviour at the beginning of courtship, when the partners are still looking for and recognizing each other, is usually quite flexible, conforming to variable conditions and circumstances. However, as they finally meet, the exchange of signals becomes more stereotyped, as if the love game were acquiring more rigorous rules toward the finish. This is well justified. Should the climax of courtship — the mating act — lead to conception, it is of utmost importance that both the male and the female play their roles precisely and correctly. In animals that reproduce by copulation, female co-operation is essential, so that she will reach full responsiveness at the same time that the male's sexual excitement climaxes. Requirements for exact synchronisation are even more crucial in animals that procreate by means of external fertilization, i.e. when the sperm meets the egg cell outside the mother's body. Any delay in emission of the reproductive cells may cause their accidental dispersal before they have a chance to meet. Therefore, many animals have evolved elaborate nuptial rituals with strict rules that ensure the correct performance of the mating act and minimize the possibility of error.

72

The spawning of salmon, carp and other fish are the best known examples of the ancient method of procreation by external fertilization, which is used by many aquatic vertebrates. In the simplest case, the female, excited by the presence and touches of the male, releases her spawn in water. The male subsequently fertilizes the eggs with his sperm. The insemination of the eggs and their further development are then left to chance. Hence, the fish must produce enormous quantities of eggs; a female carp, for example, produces 500,000 eggs, the turbot about a million, and the Atlantic cod spawns as many as eight and a half million eggs. There are, however, quite a few fish that do not abandon their eggs to fate. The male sunfish (*Lepomis*) prepares a kind of nest on the sandy bottom of a stream or lake, into which the female lays her eggs. The spawning in this genus is preceded by a special nuptial dance that varies according to species, and which is accompanied by acoustic signals. The male then guards his prospective family. The continual fanning of his fins over the eggs benefits them by bringing oxidized water

PROMENADE À DEUX

Mating without copulation

The male of the cichlid *Aequidens pulcher* guards the eggs which the female has laid on the bottom and brings fresh oxidized water to them by fanning his fins.

One part of the courtship ceremony in the paradise fish (*Macroporus opercularis*) is the formation of a bubble nest underneath which the pair spawn and in which the eggs are incubated.

The male of the three-spined stickleback (*Gasterosteus aculeatus*) responds to the presence of a gravid female by a typical zig-zag dance. His jerking movements stimulate the female to approach him and to show him her swollen silvery belly. Upon recognizing her encouragement, the male turns away from the female and swims toward his hollowed-out nest, which he has constructed of fragments of aquatic vegetation. The female follows him, and with special movements, the male indicates the nest entrance to her. When she enters the nest, he entices her to spawn by touching her protruding tail while wagging his body. Then he finishes the ceremony by swimming through the nest to fertilize the eggs.

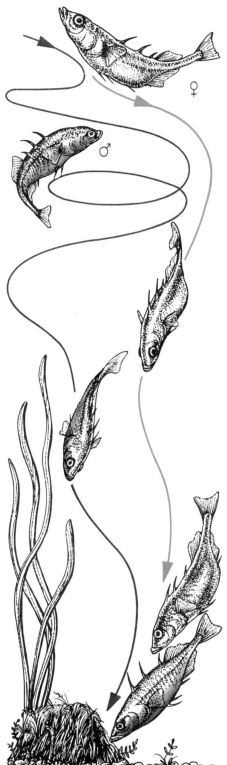

to them. After the fry hatch, the father continues to lead his young school for some time. More elaborate nests are built by sticklebacks, cichlids or paradise fish, and their nuptial ceremonies are likewise considerably more complex. Because of its memorable display, the stickleback (*Gasterosteus*) is an often used example.

If one member of the courting pair of sticklebacks leaves out any part of his or her role in the ceremony, the other does not continue. A male will not lead the female toward his nest unless she first responds to his courtship dance. This ensures that neither partner will rush the sequence and release his or her reproductive cells prematurely.

The bitterling (*Rhodeus sericeus*), a small gaily-coloured fish occurring all over Europe, became a textbook example for its peculiar way of reproduction. At the onset of the spawning season, the female develops a long yellowish or red ovipositor with which she lays her eggs inside the mantle cavity of a clam or mussel. The ceremony is also attended by the male, who simultaneously spreads his milt, which is drawn into the shell chamber by the mussel's respiration opening and fertilizes the eggs. The fry remain in the protection of the mussel until they exhaust the reserves in their yolk sac. The larvae of the mussel, in turn, often parasitize on the gills of the adult bitterlings. The mollusc and the fish thus make an equal exchange in raising each other's offspring.

Some gobies are also known for their unusual nuptial habits. The male of the common European bullhead (*Cottus gobio*) waits at the entrance to his burrow between stones. When a female swims by, he darts at her, taking her head into his huge mouth. Only a sexually mature female will tolerate this forward behaviour, remaining quiet and allowing the male to drag her to his burrow, where spawning takes place. The male then takes diligent charge of the eggs, driving off approaching fish much larger than himself. If the male bullhead pounces on an immature female, she wriggles free. The male can thus quickly test the sexual status of a female by this uncouth tactic, ensuring that he takes only a mature 'bride'.

Sharks and viviparous fish are exceptional among the lower vertebrates for their method of fertilization. They mate by copulating, and consequently their embryos develop inside the mother's body. The transfer of sperm is helped along by a copulatory organ that evolved from the male's ventral or anal fin, and which develops at maturation.

The nuptial dance of common guppies (*Poecilia reticulata*) can be witnessed even in a home aquarium, but few people are privileged to see the mating of sharks. The act was probably first observed in the short-nosed grey reef shark of the genus

a
b
c
d

The females of the tropical cichlid fish of the genus *Haplochromis* collect the spawned eggs in their mouth. For fertilization ever to take place, the male must trick the female into opening her mouth. He has orange spots on his transparent anal fin which strongly resemble real eggs in colour and shape. As the female attempts to collect these last 'forgotten' eggs, the male jets his milt directly into her mouth. The size and number of the anal fin spots is a species specific character (a–d).

Carcharhinus by Dr. Eugenia Clark in the Red Sea in 1974. A female separates from the group and a male chases her; during the chase the male bites her body and fins, inflicting deep and numerous wounds which, fortunately, heal quickly. This violent courtship is needed to induce mating. The female's hide is twice as thick as the male's, as if Nature were giving her protection against her suitor's less than gentle advances. One female reportedly got such deep 'love bites' that it appeared her tail might fall off. The first advances in the love acts of other sharks are similarly rough. During copulation the sharks swim parallel to each other, their bodies and tail plastered against one another and moving in harmony like a single monster with two heads.

Until now we have not mentioned the sense of smell in fish and sharks, but in fact it is extraordinarily acute, serving them primarily in their search for food. There is also, however, a wealth of evidence that olfactory signals are important for their nuptial dialogues. The Mexican blind cavefish *Anoptichthys jordani* or the blind goby *Typhlogobius californiensis* depend exclusively on smell when looking for a mate. In an experiment with the frillfin goby (*Bathygobius soporator*), scientists found out that an isolated male could be induced to courtship simply by adding to his tank water from the tank of a gravid female. His behaviour changes within ten seconds, a testimony to the fragrant charms of a female fish. It is noteworthy that some carp and catfish even make use of a contact chemical sense in their sex lives, tasting each other's body surface with their lips.

Descendants of the fish, the amphibians, began the venture onto land as the first vertebrates. This new way of life called for progressive changes in their mating behaviour. Evolution of new mating techniques put an end to the wasting of reproductive cells which characterizes the spawning of fish.

When a gravid female toad (*Bufo*) is clasped by the male behind her front legs, she arches her back into a typical lordosis position. The male responds to this by forming a 'basket' with his hind legs and there the discharged eggs are collected and fertilized.

The spermatophore is a capsule that serves to transfer the sperm. Fertilization by means of the spermatophore has evolved in many species independently, namely in invertebrates such as arachnias, cephalopods and some insects.

Newts solved the problem of mating in an original way. They developed a method of internal fertilization, and yet the male does not directly transfer his sperm to the female by copulation. Instead, he fastens clusters of his spermatozoids to the bottom of the pond by means of a jelly secretion, thus making a spermatophore. The female picks it up with her genital opening, which is called the cloaca.

Mating in newts is not at all a simple act. When the male encounters a female, the first thing he does is sniff intently at her cloacal region. By doing this, he can apparently assess her breeding condition and readiness for mating. The female tends to shy away at first. The male attempts to stay in her path, displaying the brilliant colouration of his belly and crest of his tail, which has become enlarged for the spring mating season. Facing the female, he hops backward while waving with his tail, which is bent forward. The purpose of these movements is to excite the female and to convince her of his virility; those males carrying the largest amounts of sperm display the most vigorously. The male appeals to several of his intended mate's senses: he enthralls her with his striking colouration, he wafts his special scent toward her with his jazzed up tail fin, and produces peculiar vibrations while dancing. This showing off gives the female an opportunity to make sure he belongs to her own species. The male nuptial displays distinctly differ from species to species. For instance, the smooth newt (*Triturus vulgaris*) male always fans his tail exactly six times a second, while the male of a related species, the palmate newt (*T. helveticus*), which lives in the same habitat, fans his tail 12 times a second.

After a while a receptive female reveals her friendly intentions and her interest in proceeding with the love dialogue. She not only stops avoiding the male, but she even starts to slowly approach him. It is now the male's turn to back away, still facing her and never ceasing to dance. It looks as if he wants to confirm her interest

The male of the smooth newt (*Triturus vulgaris*) has a conspicuous dorsal crest during the breeding season.

by extending the game. After 30 seconds or so, he turns around and gradually moves away. After travelling several centimetres, he stops and slowly waves his tail. The female, who has been following him, then touches his tail with her snout. For the male, this is a signal to elevate his tail and release his spermatophore. If the female fails to tickle his tail, he turns around to face her and patiently repeats his display. As we can see, the male does not carelessly leave his spermatophore. The female must unambiguously show her responsive state.

77

After the formation of the spermatophore, the male moves slightly away. This leaves room for the female, who follows him, to stand with her cloaca directly above the sperm capsule, which she draws inside her. The entire mating sequence is repeated two or three times, which increases the chances that at least one spermatophore will reach its intended destination despite the hit-or-miss manner.

Similar methods of indirect sperm transfer can be found among terrestrial arthropods. One thing is common to all of them; the male always forms his spermatophore on a stalk. The females, however, have a variety of approaches for obtaining the spermatophore from the male and acquiring its contents. In the simplest cases, for example in the primitive springtails (Collembola), pseudoscorpions or oribatid mites, the male does not care about the fate of his spermatophores. He simply makes lots of them in the absence of the female, and takes a chance that she will stumble across some of them. Sometimes these stalked droplets are so numerous and dense that they resemble mould. The female is apparently attracted to them by smell.

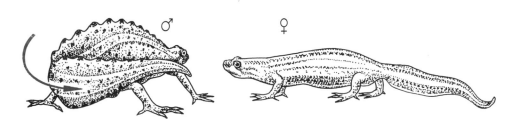

Courting male newts of the genus *Triturus* wave their tail toward the female. Frequency of the movements is species specific.

Males of some springtail species often return to their 'love gardens' and eat the old, unclaimed semen droplets, replacing them with fresh ones; the sperm remains viable for only a few hours. This curious behaviour was first noted by Victor Lemoine over a century ago, but he misinterpreted it: in 1883 he reported to the French Society for Advancement of Science that the male takes the sperm into his mouth and transfers it directly into the female's vulva.

In the springtail *Sinella curviseta,* a unique kind of sex pheromone was discovered. In the female's lifetime, there are repeated periods of fertility. The onset of each cycle is marked by her increased interest in the male's spermatophores, lasting some twenty hours. During this period the female releases a substance that stimulates the male to triple his production. For all this extra effort, the only apparent reward the male gets is a whiff of the female's perfume.

Many other male arthropods are not so reckless about the fate of their spermatophores and use numerous techniques to help the female find their sperm. In a bark inhabiting millipede, *Polyxenus lagurus,* the male weaves long, silken webs with his spermatophore at the end of the lines. The female, attracted by the silky trail, is led toward the sperm. However, the perfumed signal threads do not excite only females but also attract males. When a male finds the sperm drops of his predecessor, he will eat them and replace with fresh sperm droplets of his own. Much the same are the fragile love-snares set by males of bristletails, centipedes and some primitive pseudocropions whenever females are close by.

One of the largest European springtails, *Tetrodontophora bialiensis,* can often be found on the surface of shaded forest pools, where these clumsy insects easily drop.

Love-making in centipedes (Chilopoda) is another variation on the same theme. After a short tactile prelude the male usually spins a web and deposits in it a bean-shaped spermatophore which the closely following female takes up. The web is not only a support for the sperm but also a signal for the receptive female. The male common scutigera (*Scutigera coleoptrata*), however, takes a more active part in the sperm transfer. After a long courtship he places a spermatophore right on the ground and then pushes the waiting female with his long antennae and legs towards the sperm packet. To top off the strange love act he finally transfers the spermatophore actively with his mouth into the genital opening of his mate.

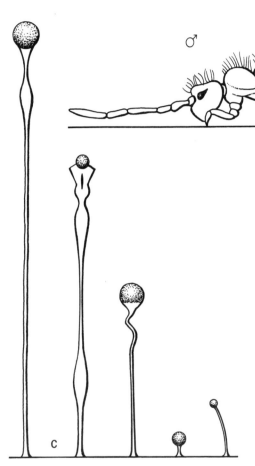

A diagram of fertilization in the springtails: The male deposits the spermatophore (a), which the female picks up with her vulva (b). Different species have spermatophores of different shapes (c).

The most active and initiative lovers can be found among the evolutionarily advanced families of springtails, pseudoscorpions and scorpions. A hundred years have passed since a friend of Charles Darwin, Sir John Lubbock, wondered over the way males of some springtails 'are very attentive to the females, and caress them lovingly with their antennae'. This is an account of his observation of a courting pair of springtails: 'It is very amusing to see these little creatures coquetting together. The male, which is much smaller than the female, runs around her, and they butt one another, standing face to face, and moving backward and forward like two playful lambs. Then the female pretends to run away and the male runs after her, with a queer appearance of anger; gets in front and stands facing her again; then she turns coyly round, but he, quicker and more active, scuttles round too, and seems to whip her with his antennae; then for a bit they stand face to face, play with their antennae, and seem to be all in all to one another.' This description of the nuptial ceremony lacks the most important point, however. The male leads his partner to the place where he formed his spermatophore. There the female sucks his sperm into her genitals. Diverse ways are used by the males to make this act easier for the females. A sminthurid male locks his antennae to those of the female by means of special hooks, and the pair dances until the female picks up all the stalked gifts he has prepared for her. The courtship behaviour of the male *Dicyrtomina minuta* is even more remarkable. From time to time, he approaches the female and gently touches her with his antennae. If he finds her willing to sit quietly for a while, he starts to act; he encircles her with a fence of stalked spermatophores.

A scorpion male's role at mating is an uneasy task. To approach a female equipped with fearsome-looking claws and a sharp, curving stinger with a venom gland at the end of her swift and nimble tail requires much caution and courage, even if one's intentions are purely sexual. There is a real risk of the male being regarded as prey rather than a suitor. It is no wonder he greets his would-be mate with great care, ready to explain his intentions and avoid misunderstandings by an

A courtship dance of a scorpion of the genus *Heterometrus* of southeast Asia.

elaborate nuptial ritual. His first manoeuvre is to neutralize her weapons by grabbing her pincers with his own. Locked together, he violently begins to dance with her. They move backward and forward with their tails held upright, sometimes intertwined. The male of the common European scorpion *Euscorpius italicus* will even repeatedly sting the female on the joint behind her pincers. After this exciting prelude, which may last several hours, the dancing ground is cleared of much of its debris. The male then extrudes the packet of sperm in an elaborate spermatophore which he deposits on the clean ground. Then, still holding the female by her claws, he jerks and heaves her forward until the sexual opening on her underside is brought directly above the sperm packet. She takes it up and the partners disengage. Occasionally, the departure may not have a happy end. While the male is still intoxicated with love, he may momentarily forget to be cautious, giving the female the chance to eat him for her wedding supper.

A tick male, although much smaller than the female, is not in danger while 'on the prowl'. He has, however, a problem of different kind. He has no penis, yet he must fertilize his mate while she is engorged into the skin of her host with her long snout. His male ancestors have evolved a truly remarkable technique to solve this dilemma. Once the male is under the female, he wriggles his "nose" into her vagina and enlarges the orifice by pushing and heaving with all his might. Then he turns around and deposits a packet of sperm beneath her orifice. After turning back around, he picks it up, and stuffs it as deeply as possible into her genitals by pushing it with his snout and tapping it with his forelegs.

WHERE DID THE ROOSTER LEARN TO DANCE?

Mating in birds

The cloaca is a common outlet of the digestive, excretory and genital organs.

A courted peahen is literally in the focus of the male's parabolically curved tail.

Viewed through our eyes, the intimate moments of animal lives often seem to be cumbersome and problem-filled. When we consider the subject of love-making in animals such as the limbless snakes, armoured tortoises, spiny hedgehogs or the heavyweights such as rhinos and elephants, our question is likely to be 'How do they do it?' These animals, just like the rest of the creatures that inhabit land, have to copulate in order to fertilize their eggs. For terrestrial animals, it is the most practical way of reproducing. Successful copulation, however, calls for perfect harmony between a couple. Otherwise, the courtship ends in rape. To guarantee the prevention of such an occurrence between copulating pairs, there had to evolve a system of unambiguous signals to be exchanged between the partners. These signals also serve to synchronize individual phases of courtship. They are often derived from behavioural elements that originally had no bearing on sexual behaviour.

An entertaining example of a creature with complex ritualized courtship signals is the cock of the domestic fowl (*Gallus gallus domesticus*). The cock starts his love proposals by prancing in waltz step among the flock of hens to test their receptivity. In front of the female of his choice, he scratches the ground while slowly backing up. He then clutches a pebble or a piece of grain in his beak, bends forward, and entices the hen to peck at the offered 'food'. His food call sounds similar to the one used by the female to call her chicks when she has found something to eat. If the female takes interest in the offering, it is not because she is hungry. By acknowledging his gift, she lets him know that she understands his proposal. She expresses her agreement by crouching. Only after receiving this invitation can the cock mount her, grasp her crest in his beak and make treading movements on her back. If the female is won over by these charming manners, she will tilt her tail sideways, exposing her cloaca and enabling a connection with the male's cloaca. The ejaculation of sperm takes only a second. A few moments later, the cock is back on the ground, announcing to his harem that the deed is done with a flapping of his wings. Within a few minutes, he may perform his excited waltz in front of another hen.

According to an old anecdote, the wife of President Calvin Coolidge noticed the enviable activity of a cock while visiting a farm, and she could not help teasing her husband on the subject. He then turned to the farmer and slyly inquired: 'Does the rooster mate with the same hen every time?' As a result of this alleged story ethologists call the phenomenon, in which switching partners increases the male's potency, the Coolidge effect.

The courtship of other gallinaceous birds is likewise based on ritualized food calls. Thus the cock of the ring-necked pheasant (*Phasianus colchicus*) pecks the ground without picking anything up and, in contrast to the domestic cock, spreads his wings and tail. The Himalayan monal pheasant (*Lophophorus impejanus*) takes the ritualization one step further, merely indicating the pecking. When the female approaches, he also spreads his wings and feathery tail. The most ritualized courtship of all is seen in the peacock (*Pavo cristatus*). The peacock indicates pecking only by a slight nod of the head, which nevertheless demonstrates that his ancestors originally must have lured females by courtship feeding. However, the main courtship signal of today's peacocks is a rhythmical shaking of the tail coverts, which have enlarged over the time to entirely cover their relatively short tails. Thus the original food call signal has developed into a spectacular display of greatly enlarged and colourful tail feathers.

The hen for whom the peacock is making such a show has some interesting behaviour herself. An observer unfamiliar with the symbolism of animal language may be surprised by the icy indifference with which she calmly pecks the ground in

front of her excited suitor. One must not be deceived by her cool exterior, however. A closer look will reveal that she pecks most intensely when standing directly in front of the cock, in the focus of his elegant parabolic train. By doing this, she lets the cock know she is not cold to his proposals. And he is well aware of it. He lets it be known by gradually increasing the quivering waves of his ornate feathery fan. Had the hen turned her back on him from the onset of courtship, she would have given him the message that she truly did not want him, and he would soon fold down his tail feathers. If, however, the female offers him her back after a positive symbolic dialogue, he also folds his feathers. This time it is for a different reason: the spread tail would hinder him during the copulation that ensues.

None of the male gallinaceous birds are exemplary husbands by our standards. The most able of the cocks in the population own large harems of hens, taking no interest in the care of their offspring. They are not choosy about the looks and behaviour of their would-be mates; in captivity, they will even mount a taxidermist's model of a female.

As we have learned already, most other birds live in monogamous pairs, and their relationship may last their whole lives. In such a case, the right choice of partner is of utmost importance. Living in monogamy brings a lot of advantages and saves many troubles. Most of us know what a risky and energy-consuming business it is looking for a partner. Imagine then how advantageous it is for animals if the partners do not need to repeat the cycle of approaching a mate, overcoming his or her aggressive tendencies, and learning his or her idiosyncrasies. It saves precious time, particularly when the breeding season is short. Neither does courtship have to be so pompous and conspicuous, so consequently does not draw the attention of predators. In addition, there is an obvious advantage in both parents being able to share in the care of their brood.

In species that are perennial monogamists, copulation is more than just a way of fertilizing the eggs — it also contributes to pair bond maintenance. The relationship

Among the pheasants, one of the most beautiful is the golden pheasant (*Chrysolophus pictus*). The male attempts to impress his mate by the splendour of the feathery fans on his temples. When courting her, he persistently circles around her, opening the fan on the side of his head that faces her.

82

between the pair is also strengthened by other means. A common method in many birds is the so-called courtship feeding. In the original form, the male really feeds his mate; therefore the female does not have to waste energy looking for food. Instead, she can accumulate large quantities of nutrients for producing the eggs in a short time, without having to leave the nest and expose herself to predators. In various bird species, however, the original courtship feeding has undergone a complex evolution, and become reduced and ritualized into a mere symbol. Male gulls and terns still ceremoniously give food to their partners, but the amount is negligible in comparison with the actual needs of the female. The Bohemian waxwing (*Bombycilla garrulus*) only gives a symbolic berry to the female, and the male love bird (*Agapornis*) merely 'offers' the female a nut which remains firmly in his beak. Surprisingly the cuckoos, which do not feed their own young, perform the feeding ritual at courtship. The flirting of many parrots, when the pair touch each other's beak as if kissing, is nothing else but ritualized feeding.

The way to a lover's heart may not always be through the stomach. Many plumed partners avow their affections and faithfulness by behaviour derived from nest building. The Australian diamond dove (*Geopelia cuneata*), a favourite exotic pet, gives the female he is courting a straw as a symbol of nest material. It is as if to say that he is vowing to provide her with earnest assistance as a nest builder.

The male king penguin (*Aptenodytes patagonica*) has a charming way of making his intentions known. He picks up a pebble or a small piece of driftwood and solemnly lays it before a bird that is standing alone. If the subject of his wooing gives him an outraged peck and squares up for a fight, he knows he has addressed another male. It is not a case of stupidity, but merely that male and female penguins look very much alike. When the male's offer is met with total indifference, then he encountered a female who either is not ready to breed or is already engaged. He picks up his spurned present and moves on until he receives a deep bow in response

When the courting partners of the black-headed gull (*Larus ridibundus*) turn their heads away from each other, it does not mean they are not interested in each other. On the contrary, it is an appeasement gesture. Showing the beak and the black mask would mean aggression.

to his gift; this tells him that finally he has found his true companion. He bows in return, and the two stretch their necks upward to trumpet a nuptial duet in celebration of their meeting.

A strong contender for the most remarkable and elaborate of bird courtships is that of the lovely European water bird, the great crested grebe (*Podiceps cristatus*). The male and female look alike, and both display their complex rituals on and under the water. The partners emerge from the water in unison with strands of aquatic plants in their beaks and present them to one another with their necks

stretched low on the water. At the climax of the ceremony, they abruptly rear up side by side, treading water with their feet until it looks as though they are standing on the surface, and rub necks from side to side. The performance is accompanied by a peculiar song; it has long been a mystery as to whether it is a solo or a duet, so perfect is their marital harmony.

Extremely complex and elaborate vocalizations have evolved in many tropical birds. Their songs are called duets. The birds use them to recognize their partners and to stay in touch with each other. In the simplest case, both partners sing the same melody, either in unison or as an echo, with the delay of the second singer being perhaps only a few miliseconds. In another instance, the melodies of each mate differ and complement each other, as in a two-part song. The most thrilling are the wedding hymns of an African shrike, the tropical boubou (*Laniarius aethiopicus*). The first part is sung by the male, the second by the female, the third by the male and so on with each partner taking a turn. Each pair has a repertoire that may contain 15 or more songs. Should a bird lose its mate by accident, it would carry on by singing not only his or her own part, but also that of the deceased mate.

The duet, or antiphonal, song is typical of monogamous species of birds in which both sexes look alike. It assures the synchronization of the partners' reproductive cycles in the tropics, where, unlike in the temperate zone, there are no climatic

Two fighting pheasant cocks (*Phasianus colchicus*) resemble freestyle wrestlers. The hen (at left) pays no attention to the enraged fighters.

84

seasonal changes to provide this kind of regulation. Birds are not the only ones that use duets. The siamang (*Symphalangus syndactylus*) and the monogamous rodent, the patagonian cavy (*Dolichotis patagona*), also sing in tandem.

A different but no less worthy approach to bond maintenance belongs to geese (*Anser*) and shelducks (*Tadorna*). Essentially these are intolerant and aggressive birds, but with the aid of special behaviour they can divert their aggression away from their own family and discharge it on others. If a female shelduck spies a stranger approaching their territory, she goads her mate into attacking by making

peculiar head movements and growling in a low-pitched voice. The male obediently darts at the intruder with his wings lowered and his neck thrust forward. When he returns to his mate, she is also in danger of being attacked by him, for he is still enraged. At the last moment, however, he stops, stretches his head up — an appeasement gesture — and both partners celebrate the victory by loud honking known as the triumphal ceremony. A pair of shelducks can easily be provoked into this behaviour by being played a recording of voices of another pair of shelducks.

The best known symbol of steadfast marital devotion is not the goose but rather the dove. The doves' reputation was known even 2,000 years ago, when Aristotle wrote about them. Recently, scientists have scrutinized the depth of the birds' faithfulness with laboratory experiments. They chose the turtle dove (*Streptopelia turtur*) for their investigation, pairing off young birds and allowing them to nest in separate cages for one season. At the end of the breeding season, the pairs were separated and all the birds kept in isolation for eight months. Then tests were performed to find out whether the original couples would still recognize each other after such a passage of time and whether they would retain their affection for each other. Groups of three males and three females were placed together in large outdoor cages, each bird having his or her original partner among its group. The ornithologists then recorded with whom the birds mated, built a nest and incubated the eggs. The results left one in no doubt that doves recognize their partners even after a long separation and in unfamiliar surroundings: all the birds, without exception, paired with the one they had nested with the previous season in the laboratory.

Doves also served as experimental subjects for studying the effects of male behaviour on the reproductive physiology of the female. The male's cooing and head-bobbing induces development of the female's gonads, even if the pair are caged with a glass partition between them. The presence of the male and his courtship display have generally profound effects on the production of sex hormones in the female, which in turn activate her sexual receptivity, egg production, and all the instincts associated with nest construction, incubation of eggs and care of the young. The physiologically caused unwillingness of the female to mate at the beginning of the breeding season protects her from being deserted by the male prematurely, and at the same time gives her plenty of opportunities to make sure the partner she has chosen is willing and able to share the parental duties ahead.

The love dialogue in birds does not generally break off after copulation. The couple, still caught up in the excitement of mating, must cool down. Various appeasement gestures and comforting activities known as post-copulatory behaviour serve this purpose. Gulls turn their beaks away from each other, terns feed one another after copulation, grey herons cross their long necks several times in succession and then the male offers the female a dry twig as a symbol of nest material. Perhaps the most varied post-copulatory displays are those described in various ducks. The most conspicuous ones are given names by ethologists such as 'head-up, tail-up', or 'nod-swimming', reflecting the amusing movements of the contented drake. These post-copulatory activities are important for keeping the home fires burning in the marriages of monogamous feathery pairs.

The symbolic 'kisses' which can be observed in a pair of collared turtle doves (*Streptopelia decaocto*) and some other birds is a ritualized feeding behaviour serving to maintain the pair bonds.

The triumphant ceremony is a common behaviour in geese. The male creates small symbolic skirmishes with other birds on purpose or even attacks inanimate objects he would normally ignore, just to have an excuse to celebrate a victory together with his mate (bottom). In this way one of the most enduring marital bonds known among animals is maintained and strengthened.

Mating of mute swans (*Cygnus olor*) is a spectacular sight.

The courtship behaviour of the common goldeneye drake (*Bucephala clangula*) is one of the most conspicuous and best investigated epigamic behaviours in ducks. Striking movements and postures are displayed also after copulation as part of the drake's post-copulatory ceremony.

Males of some birds, namely ducks and ostriches, have a penis which protrudes stiffly from the cloaca when the bird is aroused. It is not a tube-like organ but a fleshy rod with a deep groove through which the sperm flows.

In some monogamous bird species rather complicated relationships between the sexes have been observed. Certain ducks belong to these. Although the drake will stay 'married' to his female (at least as long as she lays her eggs), he will often try to force himself on any female he sees. Surprisingly, the husband of the assaulted duck may not protect his spouse from such advances, but if she is being chased by a strange male, he may go along to make sure he does not lose her in the commotion. For her part, however, she behaves as if she would rather die than be unfaithful and may spend a long time hiding in the grass to avoid the interloper.

Some geese, on the other hand, handle such problems differently and may readily form triangles. In fact, two males can establish a homosexual pair, and when they are courting, a female may suddenly interpose between them and be quickly fertilized. If she is accepted by them, the three can be seen together several weeks later attending to their offspring.

The mating habits of the ostrich may seem to be a puzzle to us. Males regularly court several females yet only one hen can be observed on the nest and later leading the chicks. The truth is quite strange. The male ostrich defends a large territory and acquires a female who lays her eggs in a nest scrape. Several days later other hens come and contribute to the original clutch with their own eggs. The first, or major, female gets readily off the nest to let the latecomers in, but only she and the male sit on the eggs. Eventually there are up to forty eggs in the nest. Since one bird cannot

A courting male white stork (*Ciconia ciconia*) accompanies his nuptial pantomime with a loud clapping of his beak.

Courting herons, storks and egrets express their moods and intentions by characteristic movements and displays. Their aristocratic bodies are literally made for this way of communication. Perhaps this is why they are a favourite subject of nature photographers. This kind of bird pantomime has been well documented in the American green heron (*Butorides virescens*), which nests in large colonies in swampy areas, often near large cities. These birds like to build their nest on dead trees standing amidst the swamp. On arrival from the winter quarters, the males distribute themselves among suitable trees and each occupied tree is then defended against other males. When the females arrive, the behaviour of the males suddenly changes. Each male attempts to attract a female to his tree by a typical, pleasant sounding voice. A singing bird stretches his neck upward, pointing his beak backward away from the female, as if to show his friendly intentions. Scientists call this behaviour the stretch display. It can be found also in the repertoire of the courting males of the European grey heron (*Ardea cinerea*), as shown in the opposite picture.

cover them properly, some get pushed to the edge. The major hen can somehow recognize her own eggs and she will move the eggs of the other females to the edge to make a buffer against predators from them. A jackal or vulture cannot consume all the eggs (or later chicks), so the extra ones reduce the chances of the major hen's offspring being eaten. What advantage have the minor hens from this arrangement? Although they have failed to gain a cock with whom to rear their chicks, by laying in another ostrich's nest, there still is the chance that at least a few of their eggs will survive to hatch.

In a common European bird, the dunnock (*Prunella modularis*), the relationships between the sexes are unusually variable and complicated. Male dunnocks delineate territories in the spring, and only later the females set up their own feeding ranges. If a female's range is within the territory of one male, she will mate only with him. Her monogamous way of life is, however, quickly forgotten, if her range overlaps two male territories. She needs a large range when food is scarce, and it will then be more likely to overlap two territories, with the advantage that both males will help her to feed her young. Another complication is that a male may share his territory with a smaller subordinate male who remains unobtrusively in dense cover. The dominant male tries to insure his paternity of the eggs by guarding the female as she is approaching the laying, and spends as much as half of his time chasing the other male. Vicious fights can break out and the subordinate dunnock may be killed. However, with a bit of luck, he may also manage to mate when the dominant male has lost sight of the female.

89

HOW CAN HEDGEHOGS MAKE LOVE WITHOUT STABBING THEMSELVES?

The use of smell for the purpose of sex in vertebrates

As we have seen, the gorgeous pheasant and similarly handsome cocks are well endowed with opportunities to express themselves. In contrast, the lowly, limbless snake seems sadly lacking. The general view is that their only performing talent is their hiss. It is true that this dismaying sound can often save their lives. But in inter-snake communication, it is hardly of any importance for snakes have poor hearing. Then what other signals does the snake language contain? At the onset of courtship, scent and sight play important roles by helping individuals to discriminate members of their own species, and most particularly to find the opposite sex. Once two snakes find each other, the conversation that follows is carried out mainly by means of touch. The love-making of snakes is a perfect concert of undulating movements and lilting touches. When we consider the limits imposed on a long, smooth, limbless snake's body, the unique expression of these animals must fascinate us. They are able to perform various acts by different portions of their lengthy bodies, either simultaneously or successively. These acts allow the partners to tell each other everything for which others need a voice, conspicuous feathers or a complex repertoire of scents. Of course, the details of sexual intercourse differ in various species, but most snakes keep to a common protocol. The male usually tries first to get onto the back of the female, while vigorously stroking his chin against various parts of her body. His body weaves from her head to her tail or from her tail to her head in an apparent effort to pacify his partner and get himself in parallel alignment with her body. Next, the muscles in various parts of his body start to jerk and ripple. His restless tail constantly stimulates her genital region. She responds by broadly opening her cloaca, allowing the male to introduce his engorged copulatory organ. While locked in this embrace, he transfers his sperm into her.

Even such clumsy lovers as turtles have a surprisingly rich vocabulary of expressions for the purpose of sex. In ways similar to those of snakes, tortoises can recognize individuals of their own species, but of different sex, by their smell. A courting male regularly sniffs at the female's cloaca. In some species, the sex pheromones are produced by a special subdentary gland on the chin. During courtship, the animals smear their pheromones over the scales on their forelegs, which are then offered to the partner to smell. Water turtles, on the contrary, are guided by their sight when looking for a mate. Tortoises often communicate also by means of various noises, since they have good hearing. However, the most elaborate part of the tortoises' love-dialogue occurs when they touch each other.

The initial phase of the mating behaviour in the American garter snake (*Thamnophis melanogaster*) is called chin rubbing.

Strangely enough, the shell constitutes no obstacle for this, but the kind of touch they use somehow belies the intimacy of the situation. It consists mainly of biting the legs, and all sorts of shell ramming, which in the case of large tortoises can be heard up to 100 metres away. Sometimes the male locates the female's cloacal opening with the tip of his tail before attempting to join their genitals. As a rule, the

Mating of the Galapagos giant tortoise (*Geochelone elephantopus*).

first attempts to copulate are not successful, because the female is anything but co-operative with a strange male. The union is consummated only after several days of living together, and following many patient and fruitless attempts on the part of the male. It may be that the male's presence is necessary for inducing the proper hormonal conditions in the female, and that only by his protracted courtship will he prepare her reproductive organs for a proper function. We have already seen this in birds.

Among mammals, long-lasting monogamous bonds are the exception rather than the rule. Therefore, the first concern of most mammals at the beginning of the breeding season is to find a mate. This is done almost exclusively by means of smell. We have already learned that the scent marks made by urine, faeces or secretions from special skin glands, which the animal leaves behind, have a broad significance. They disclose practically everything an animal should know about his or her partner before mating: to what species it belongs, its sex and age, what is the partner's social status and in which clan and colony it belongs and, last but not least, his or her physiological state and momentary moods. If the animals are in the habit of remaining solitary within a certain territory, one of the pair (usually the male) must leave his territory and convince the female he selects that he has no aggressive intentions towards her. Again he does this with scented messages, which he distributes over the visited territory. Visual, acoustic or touch stimuli are of use only at very short distances.

The behaviour of animals searching for a mate is as varied as the living habits of the different mammalian species. But copulation and the preliminaries are much the same among the majority of mammals. Why not use, as an example of a mammalian copulative act, a rather primitive insectivorous species, the well-known but almost mythical hedgehog?

These spiny fellows live solitary lives for most of the year. However, in the spring they go looking for one another and become embroiled in a lengthy and loud courtship. The first encounter usually does not find the female in the mood for a love game. Instead, the male meets stubborn resistance. When he repeatedly tries to sniff or lick her spiny back, she menacingly turns to face him with her head all bristled and spiny. Both animals pant heavily, and if we employed an ultrasound detector, we would also hear high-pitched squeaks. This performance may last quite a long time. The male must be truly perseverant to finally succeed in licking the female's prickly back and getting a 'taste' of her scent.

For tasting the female, the hedgehog uses his vomeronasal (Jacobson's) organ, which is an accessory organ of smell in vertebrates. This organ has an important function in the sexual life of many animal species. If the nerves leading to it are cut, this often results in the impairment of sexual behaviour of the animal.

The taste of the female pheromone apparently induces self-anointing in the male. A stream of foamy saliva rushes from his mouth and he spreads it over his shoulders toward his back. Such curious behaviour probably serves to stimulate the male himself, because it makes no visible impression on his mate. For overcoming her resistance and reluctance, the male must employ another technique. He releases a pungent secretion from his erect penis, an aphrodisiacal compound with which he splatters everything around including his partner. This smelly persuasion may have to continue for several hours, but finally the female acquiesces. She assumes what ethologist call the presentation posture: she curves down the lower part of her spine, swaying her back, smoothing down her hackled spines and exposing her genital region. All this, together with the special endowment of the male (as pictured), answer the question: 'How can hedgehogs make love without stabbing themselves?'

Urinating at the female during courtship was observed among rabbits, guinea pigs, pangolins, armadillos and agoutis. The male of the tree-dwelling North-American porcupine (*Erethizon dorsatum*) stands up during courtship and sprays short trains of urine at the female, and she responds in a similar fashion.

The chemical nature of several mammalian sex pheromones has been successfully unravelled in the past decade or so. One of them is copulin, an attractant perfume in the female rhesus monkey (*Macaca mulatta*); it not only lures the males, but also stimulates them to copulate. Copulin is a blend of five volatile fatty acids that can be easily synthesized. Another recognized mammalian scent, which has also been synthesized, is the sex pheromone of domestic pigs (*Sus domestica*). It originates from the sweat and salivary glands of a sexually excited boar. A sow in heat assumes a characteristic presentation posture when she smells the compound. The preparation has been commercially available under the trade mark Boar Mate, and farmers use it to aid artificial insemination at large pig-breeding establishments. However, the record for the longest use of an animal scent by man is held by musk. It is found in many different animal secretions, some playing an important role in the sexual life of their producers. At low concentrations, the musk scent is pleasant to our noses also. That is why it has been a valuable and sought-after perfume for at least 3,000 years, even though its chemical composition has been known for only a few decades.

The copulation of the European hedgehog (*Erinaceus europaeus*) is preceded by a long period of olfactorial stimulation (top). Only when the female assumes the so-called presentation position (centre), can the male make an attempt to copulate (bottom).

The use of sex pheromones during court-ship is a general practice among mammals. The male almost always sniffs the female before copulation and his interest focuses on her genital region, where most of the sex-specific scents are located. The picture shows the impala (*Aepyceros melampus*).

Males not only sniff the genital region and nipples of the females but they also eagerly lick those parts. After each lick the male raises his head and contorts his snout into a sort of pucker: he half-opens his mouth and exposes the teeth by curling down the lower lip. This grimace is common among many unrelated animals but can be seen most frequently in various hoofed mammals. Despite the fact that this conspicuous behaviour has been known for more than half a century and labelled in several languages as 'flehmen', we are not yet certain about all its biological functions. We are sure flehmen helps the transport of non-volatile chemosensory materials from the mouth cavity to the vomeronasal organ (Jacobson's organ), which is a unique structure able to detect and analyze scents of this kind. The picture shows a buck mouflon (*Ovis musimon*) performing flehmen.

The mention of animal pheromones in the service of human vanity spurs me to make a few deprecating remarks on behalf of our own species. A certain portion of *Homo sapiens* population can hardly imagine life without chemical deodorants. By means of various lotions, ointments or sprays, we do our best to deprive ourselves of our own natural body fragrance, by replacing it with animal musks or herbal aromas. What we are so stubbornly renouncing by doing this is one of our last ties with our animal ancestors. Today, hardly any scientist would dispute the existence of human pheromones, even though we are mostly unaware of their effects. Is not the human body equipped with the tufts of hair designed to regulate the release of its fragrant emanations? The structures are commonly believed to have no biological function in man, but if they were found on the body of a newly discovered mammalian species, such organs would undoubtedly be considered part of a pheromonal system. The steroid ketons found in the sweat glands of man's armpits are compounds that excite the noses of women more than the noses of men. Why then should we not admit the existence of male pheromones even in man? Have you not experienced an indefinable pleasure when in close proximity to that special person, a feeling you never experience in the presence of other people? And

During courtship, which can last from a few hours to 2–3 days, the male kangaroo (*Macropus*) frequently sniffs the opening of the pouch and the urogenital area of the female.

what about those human smells, which, in certain intimate situations, become exciting fragrances but are seldom mentioned because of social taboos?

Not always is it the male who initiates the mating act. The females of many mammalian species are sexy beasts when they come into heat. The female kangaroo may serve us as an example. When she wants to copulate she begins to follow a male around, staying right after him and nozzling him whenever he stops. But when the male turns to her, she looks startled and bounds away. He does not seem to be fooled by her sudden coyness and hops determinedly after her. During the chase she will close her pouch tight by special muscles if carrying a young. At last, she stops running and gives in. As the male approaches, she crouches forward and moves her large tail to one side, exposing the opening to her cloaca. The male then hugs her from behind around the waist with his short forelegs or places them tightly on her shoulders. The copulatory movements are rather unorthodox in kangaroos, because the male's penis lies behind his scrotum and so it projects downward and backward when 'erect'. Consequently, the male has to thrust downward instead of forward when he enters her from the rear.

One of the most impressive mating acts can be occassionally seen in zoos where rhinoceroses are kept. Reproduction of these armour-plated giants is a risky business in captivity, since rhinocerous courtship can be incredibly violent and so dangerous that sometimes one of the animals may be fatally wounded. When the female enters her mating period, her vulva gets swollen and, in the presence of a male, she begins to make shrill whistling noises. He responds with deep heaving sights. Then the animals begin to get a bit edgy, tossing their huge heads and trotting about nervously. As the tension gradually builds, sooner or later something has to break. This happens when the male wheels and charges his mate. She is far too powerful to be intimidated by him, and she meets his charge head-on. The force of the impact of the three-thousand-pound giants is incredible. Repeatedly the beasts rush each other, butting and hooking powerfully with their horns for about an hour. The amorous fight grows increasingly savage, and it is now that one of the exhausted lovers will likely be injured. And it is also about this time that the female will decide whether the male is worthy. If she decides to mate, she signals her willingness to cooperate by presenting her rear to the male and pulling her short tail tightly to one side, exposing her swollen vulva. This move makes the male to change his entire attitude. He moves around her and mounts her from behind. Penetration itself is a lengthy process and copulation may last over an hour. The male ejaculates about every ten minutes, having literally mounted the female with all four of his feet being off the ground. When he finally withdraws, both giants are utterly exhausted. However, they may quickly recover and the whole act may begin all over again about an hour later.

The oestrus in lions lasts only a few days. The pair, however, mate many times during this period. The lioness regularly initiates the mating act. She walks around a lion attempting to arouse him with her smell. Occasionally she slaps his face with her tail and then walks away purring. The male follows her and mounts her for several seconds. Ten to fifteen minutes later the lioness incites the lion again.

A rare spectacle in a zoo — copulation in rhinoceroses.

SLIMY LOVE

Mating in snails, cockroaches and bedbugs

With a little patient observation, you can personally witness one of Nature's most unique mating rituals. You need not travel to the tropics or to the antipodes to see this activity. Merely look in your own backyard and find two grown garden snails. There is no need to worry about which one is male and which is female. Snails are hermaphrodites; each has both male and female reproductive organs. The opening of the genitals is found in an unorthodox place — on the right side of the head, under the right optic tentacle. This opening has several functions. It serves as an entrance to the vagina, as an outlet of the finger-like sex accessory glands, and the penis is extruded through it. It also functions as an exit from which a calcareous formation called *sagita amoris,* the mysterious dart of love, is shot during the slimy love-making of two snails. But let us not get ahead of ourselves.

It is almost a miracle that the two molluscs ever find each other, with their usual, snail's pace. Perhaps it happens because even these languid animals enhance their chance of meeting by using scent as a guide. A snail which is ready to mate leaves in its slimy trace a chemical message for another snail to follow. When the two finally meet, they first communicate by touch. The challenge for each of them is to find the genital opening of their partner and to synchronize their actions. On this depends the success of mutual fertilization. However, accomplishing it may not be as easy as it sounds. It is difficult for them to position themselves on each other's limbless, slimy body. That may be why the mating of snails is a protracted and complex procedure. It consists of four phases. In phase one, the snails size each other up and search for some reference points. It is called the upright phase, because each one climbs up the foot of the other, until eventually they are reared up against one another. The lips of the mouth of one individual find the lips of the other and they remain in a long 'kiss'. As their excitement increases, the genital openings of both snails slowly enlarge. The next phase is called the down-curving phase, because both snails curve their heads toward the ground, touching only with the hind part of their soles. Remaining in this crouched position, they shoot the dart into each other's soft body. Often the dart breaks off and remains in the partner's body. In zoology textbooks, this rough behaviour is often interpreted as a strong mechanical, or perhaps even a chemical, stimulus aimed at climaxing the sexual excitement of both snails. However, this is only unproven conjecture. Results of

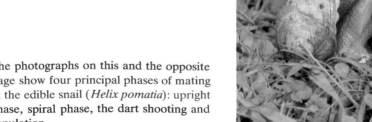

The photographs on this and the opposite page show four principal phases of mating in the edible snail (*Helix pomatia*): upright phase, spiral phase, the dart shooting and copulation.

a meticulous study which opposes this hypothesis were reported by students from the University of Copenhagen. Experimental removal of the dart before copulation did not significantly affect the course of mating.

The shooting of the dart marks the third phase, called the spiral phase. The snails again assume the vertical position, this time wound around each other. This position has a purpose, for it makes possible the alignment of their genital openings. If copulation is to be successful and lead to an exchange of their spermatophores, the intromission of both partners must take place simultaneously. Several attempts may be needed for this to happen. During the final phase, the snails rest motionless for several hours with the soles of their feet still in contact.

This short survey of the intimate animal dialogues would hardly be sufficient

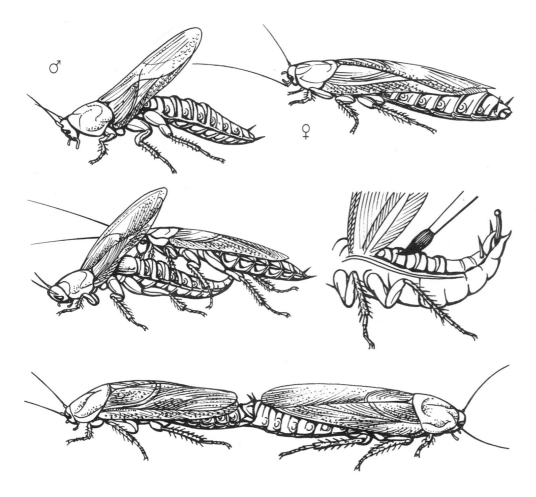

without some additional mention of insects. We have already looked at the eagerness with which the males of certain moths respond to the scent of their females. Many other insects also use sex pheromones for their carnal conversations. The private lives of various cockroaches can be an inexhaustible source of information for an insect sexologist. The common German cockroach (*Blatella germanica*) has paid for his cohabitation with man by losing all secrets about its sex life. When the female cockroach is ready for mating, she attracts the attention of males by releasing a short-range pheromone. As soon as the male gets the message, he assumes the head-to-head position with his future mate, and both partners indulge in antennal fencing. After a while the male turns his back on the female and raises his wings. This the female cockroach apparently finds most intriguing. By this posture, the male is offering his own sexual lure, which he exudes from special glands on his back. The next move in the love-play is carried out by the female, who climbs up onto his back and tastes the secretions of his dorsal glands. Now the male has the female in the right position for copulation. He elongates his abdomen and extrudes his copulatory organ from below. The latter is a rather complex instrument resembling a Swiss army knife equipped with several blades, a can-opener, screwdriver, scissors etc. One of the hooks catches the genital plate on the abdomen of the female. Then the tip of the aedeagus (the prominent part of the penis) enters the female's vagina. When this happens, the partners can turn 180° and assume a more convenient position, in which they remain for about an hour.

100

The pheromone from the dorsal glands of male cockroaches was isolated in another species, *Nauphoeta cinerea*. It was given the apt name seducine. When this pheromone is applied to a dummy cockroach which is then put into a cage full of receptive females, the latter will pounce on the perfumed decoy and lick it eagerly. *Nauphoeta* females can be provoked into such intimacies even with an extract from other cockroach species. The interest scientists have in seducin is easy to understand: they hope to find a way of using it against the interests of those for whom it was intended — the troublesome female cockroaches.

The males of several cockroach species have inherent tendencies toward homosexuality, particularly if they have been living in celibacy for a long time. A single female, released in a crowd of such males, will incite a coital frenzy among them. Curiously, they will display the same elements of courtship behaviour toward each other that are known to be used in heterosexual interactions. The female can then leisurely choose the time for mating. It is up to her to decide upon which wooer's back she will climb and taste the secretion of his dorsal glands.

By our standards, the habits of the despised bedbugs (*Cimex lectularius*) are rather perverse. Nonetheless, they are interesting. Immature nymphs as well as adult individuals call an assembly to a suitable resting place by the use of a bad-smelling compound. Evidence is still lacking that this aggregation pheromone plays any role in the love-life of the bedbug. The copulation of bedbugs is described as traumatic insemination, because the male pierces the wall of the female's abdomen with his sabre-like penis and injects his sperm directly into her body cavity. After mating, the wound quickly heals, leaving a distinct scar.

The amount of sperm injected into the blood stream of the female is enormous. The spermatozoids are carried along with the haemolymph to the reproductive organs. There they stay until the female engorges herself on a meal of sucked blood, which triggers off the ripening of the eggs in her ovaries.

A similar, strange way of mating occurs also in many parasitic or predatory relatives of the bedbugs, and some wild guesses exist about its biological meaning. It was the Italian zoologist A. Berlese who discovered this phenomenon at the beginning of this century. He wondered about the unusually high amounts of injected sperm and assumed that at least some of the spermatozoids must be absorbed by the female. Dr. Berlese was the first to propose the idea that the female might actually be nourished by the male during times of famine by 'intravenous injections', and that she may even produce some eggs without taking a blood meal.

Dr. Jacques Carayon of the National Museum of Natural History in Paris spent many years studying the sexual eccentricities of various parasitic bugs. His conclusions could not refute Berlese's theory. Males of one African species even regularly inseminate each other.

A pair of the pentatomid bugs *Graphosoma italicum* have no problems in finding each other. These insects live gregariously on umbelliferous plants. They mate often and for a long time. A courting male stimulates the female by touching her with his antennae.

The males of various leaf bugs also have fragrant sex pheromones. A typical example is the sun bug (*Eurygaster integriceps*), a serious grain pest in the Balkans and southern Russia. A male searching for a female climbs to an elevated spot, lifts up his abdomen and releases a chemical lure that smells pleasantly of vanilla. If no female responds to his fragrant call within a few minutes, the male takes off to try his luck a few metres away.

In humans, the use of perfumes is generally thought of as a feminine trait. The examples of chemical communication given in preceding chapter, however, may cause us to draw other conclusions.

Indeed, the sexually excited males of many insect species smell pleasantly to us. A century ago, the German entomologist F. Müller had already called attention to the fragrant aphrodisiacs of various butterflies, and he sometimes even wore aromatic little male butterflies as boutonnières to please his own nostrils.

Spicy and pleasant aromas are given off by the males of several heteropteran species as well. The giant water bug *Lethocerus indicus* is the best-known example. The male releases a strong-smelling liquid with a cinnamon aroma from a pair of tubular glands which may be as much as 4 cm long and some 3 mm in diameter. This liquid is used by people in southeast Asia for spicing fatty meals, and the insects may in fact owe the survival of their species to venturesome entrepreneurs who market the synthetic version of this 'buggy flavour' to cooks in that part of Asia. Recently, German chemists identified the essential component of this pheromone.

In the production of ambrosial perfumes, male bumblebees are indisputably the elite. Excretions from their mandibular glands smell splendidly of various flowers. The most common European species, *Bombus terrestris,* as one example, is redolent with the smell of roses. Males use these fragrances to mark the paths of their repeated nuptial flights through the vegetation. Their chemical calling cards are sought after by bumblebee queens. Since each species produces a different odour, the scent message is a reliable isolation mechanism in these insects.

A sweet-smelling pheromone is produced by the courting male of the exotic fruitfly *Dacus tryoni.* He also sings, if we can define as song the monotonous flute-like tone he produces with vibrations of his wings. The pheromone apparently attracts and excites the female from a distance, and the sound aids her in homing in on the alluring male. Males of a related fruitfly, *Rioxa pornia,* seduce their mates

ALL PERFUMED AND 'ON THE PROWL'

Sexual tactics of male insects

At the beginning of courtship, the male sun bug makes very gentle advances to his chosen partner. He caresses her with his antennae until she consents to further advances. Then he clings to her, side by side, extrudes his copulatory organ, the sharp tip of which eventually finds its way. The couple then assume an opposed position, in which they remain for at least two hours.

Many courtship signals have evolved from elements of feeding behaviour, care for the young, grooming (care for hairs or feathers), aggressive or defence behaviour etc. Such an evolutionary acquisition of a new function for the purpose of communicating is known as ritualization.

with a chemical that smells repugnant to us. We can get a whiff of a calling male from half a metre away. On a closer look we can discover the source of his nose-piercing pheromone — glandular pouches sticking out from the sides of his abdomen. He aids the evaporation of his sexy perfume by fanning his wings. When the female succumbs, the male offers her a foamy secretion and waits until she begins to nibble on it. Then he hops onto her back to fulfil his biological mission.

Such bribery with food in exchange for sexual favours is not at all rare in insects. The predatory male of the scorpion fly *Hylobittacus apicalis* catches a soft insect and chews it into a small ball. While he does this, two conspicuous red pouches protrude from the end of his abdomen, giving off a compound reminiscent of rancid butter. However, to the female it is an irresistible attractant. When she approaches him, the male offers her the prey. While she is attempting to take the juicy ball from him, the tip of his abdomen finds her genitals, and the couple copulate. Only then will the male give up the morsel to the female as a wedding present. The male of the scorpion fly *Harpobittacus australis* seems to be even stingier. He also lures a female with captured prey, but when he gets what he wanted he keeps his present for the next female. The nuptial feeding thus has become ritualized in this species.

The best example of the gradual ritualization of nuptial feeding, leading from food actually being exchanged to its becoming a mere symbol, can be found among the danceflies (Empididae). Many of them are predatory, and that is what the males take advantage of. Males form dense swarms in moist areas of the woods. Many of them may be seen carrying freshly killed prey. Females look for these swarms and try to pick up a male in possession of a particularly appealing snack. The lucky male is then allowed to mate with her as long as she feasts on the nuptial food.

There are several interpretations of the biological significance of this behaviour. No doubt the dainty offered by the male is a welcome contribution to the menu of a female aspiring to motherhood. From the male's standpoint, the satiation of his voracious bride's appetite is a sort of guarantee that he himself will not be eaten. On the other hand, the size of the prey the male presents is a measure of his abilities, which the female uses when selecting a father for her offspring. Males offering skimpy prey will have little hope of being paid any heed. It has been known for a male to offer two pieces of prey for the same price. In the end, the presentation of food may only be a visual stimulus that gets the male the attention he needs in order to copulate with a female. This latter assumption is strongly backed up by observations of the courtships of some danceflies that have modified their nuptial habits in various ways.

Originally, the males wrapped their prey in silken threads and sticky secretions, perhaps to prevent escape. Males of more evolutionarily advanced species encase their prey in strings of small bubbles. In still more developed species, more attention is devoted to the production of the packaging than to the contents, which may be just the remnants of a carcass. The prey serves merely as a stimulus for the male to produce the aesthetic container, and the female does not care what is in it. It is no surprise, then, that in the phylogenetically most advanced danceflies the male does not bother hunting for quarry at all, setting before the female a gorgeous but empty balloon skillfully blown from his anus. The female plays with the balloon during copulation and her predatory bent is forgotten for the moment.

The spell-binding performance of mating dragonflies and damselflies (Odonata) would most likely be given more publicity if one had to travel to, say, Loch Ness, Scotland, to see it. However, the little miracles are to be viewed on the banks of any river, lake or pond. Take a look at the huge eyes of dragonflies, which are good not only for hunting and for keeping a look out for rivals, but are also used when searching for a mate. In some damselflies the male counts on the female using her own eyes to notice the show he puts on during mating season. The male attracts the female's attention by rhythmically bending up his abdomen and displaying the luminous colouration underneath. When a female accepts this invitation to the male's territory, the male takes off and the courtship begins with an aerial whirl. During this flight, the male leads his mate to the chosen site for laying eggs, and by a sequence of distinct movements he indicates the place to her. After copulation, the female remembers this location and returns to it, this time alone, to lay her eggs. The male watches and guards her from a distance. Dragonflies (Anisoptera) have similar habits, with the difference that the male leads the female to the site of egg-laying after copulation and guards her by circling above the designated spot. Sometimes, while his first mate is busy depositing her precious burden, the male succeeds in attracting a second female, mates with her and directs her to deposit her eggs next to his first spouse. Both females get along very well while laying eggs and being guarded by their bigamous mate.

The flesh-flies of the genus *Sarcophaga* (in the picture), as well as many other related flies, check their species identity and at the same time stimulate themselves for mating by means of sex pheromones released from the waxy layer of their cuticle. In the laboratory, the males may attempt to copulate even with a wick soaked with the synthetic pheromone.

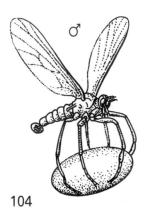
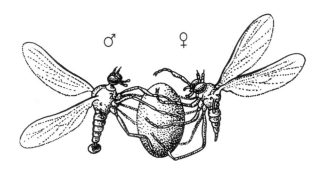

Males of the so called 'balloon flies' of the genus *Hilara* solicit the favours of the female by offering her a symbolic present, a silky balloon.

The guarding ceremony has a biological significance. To secure his paternity, the male prevents the female from leaving his territory and mating with another male before she deposits the batch of eggs he has fertilized. During copulation, the sperm is deposited in the female's spermatheca, and while the eggs are being laid, the sperm is released onto the eggs. If the female repeatedly mates without ovipositing between copulations, the sperm of the last partner has the best chance of fertilizing all the eggs, being on top and therefore closest to the outlet of the spermatheca.

Copulation in this archaic insect order is the most curious mating act among the hexapods. There is nothing extraordinary about the female's genitals; they are situated at the end of her long abdomen. The male abdomen also terminates with a genital opening, but in addition to this its tip is provided with large claspers. This would be nothing remarkable if the claspers were used to hold the genitals of the female, as happens in many other insects. However, the dragonfly's claspers are adapted for grasping the female behind the head! The females of some species even have indentations in their necks expressly for this purpose, into which the claspers fit perfectly. Of course this creates a dilemma for the mating pair: the male's claspers, with his genital opening, are at the end of the abdomen and hold the

female's neck instead of her genitals. Nature has solved the problem by endowing the male with a special bladder-like pouch on the ventral side of the second abdominal segment, from which the jointed penis comes out. Since this secondary copulatory organ does not connect with the outlets of the testes, the male has to fill it before copulation. He curves his long thin abdomen into a loop and transfers the sperm into the pouch. This done, he goes seeking his first partner. He gently lands on her back, while both are still in flight. If she is receptive, she will tolerate his advances. Then the male bends down his abdomen and grasps the female around the neck with his terminal claspers. Holding her head firmly, he releases his leg hold on her, so that the female finds herself in an odd tandem with her partner. So far she has been passive to his actions. Now it is her turn to take the initiative. The firm hold on her neck stimulates her to bend her abdomen forward and look for the male's copulatory organ with her own genitals. In the meantime, the male lands on vegetation above the water, with his partner wound up in a strange loop. This position enriched the already copious glossary of sex terminology with a new term — the wheel posture.

The little damselfly male from the family Agrionidae will not release the female after copulation and literally carries her to the oviposition site (above left). Then he holds her underwater until she deposits all her eggs (above right).

Dragonflies copulating
— the characteristic wheel posture.

It is sometimes a daring adventure for a male of a predatory arthropod species with sexual motives in mind to approach a female. He must be very cautious and state his identity and intentions clearly to prevent being mistaken for prey. In addition, he must be absolutely sure of the mood of his mate, or he may well end up dead: if the female has already mated with another male, she often loses her sexual receptivity. Then her first and only concern is how to fill her stomach.

In the course of a long evolution, males have picked up many tricks to help them impregnate a female without ending up in her mandibles. One of the tried-and-true ways of pacifying a dangerous prospective mate is to give her an edible wedding present. We have already mentioned that this scheme is used by danceflies. Another group of arthropods in which courtship feeding is well-known is the spiders. They are old hands at using food to appease one kind of appetite before satisfying another kind of hunger. Witness the common European nursery web spider (*Pisaura mirabilis*), as illustrated in the series at the top of these pages.

The males of some spider species astutely wait until the female catches food for herself and approach her only when she is preoccupied with feeding. There are other spiders (mostly of the jumping spiders family) who follow the philosophy that discretion is the better part of valour; the male finds an immature female (termed sub-adult by the arachnologists) and stands patiently near her silken shelter until she sheds her last nymphal cuticle and becomes an adult. The male takes advantage of the short period of her early adulthood when her new cuticle is still soft and her jaws are not yet a threat.

Before enumerating some of the other security measures in the sexual lives of spiders, let us consider how they copulate. Within the animal kingdom, the spiders' mating is of a rare form. The male has no penis; the genital opening is just a small slit on the underside of his abdomen. However, the outlet of the female's genitals cannot be overlooked. It is covered by a hard chitinous plate, which may be beautifully sculptured, reminiscent of a glazed ceramic creation from a gallery of modern art. This so-called epigyne has a distinctive shape for each species. It

DIRTY TRICKS

Cannibalism as a part of sex, and sexual mimicry

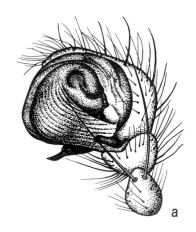

a

The male nursery web spider (*Pisaura mirabilis*) is darker and smaller than the female. Before he sets out for an amorous adventure, he catches a suitably mouth-watering prey, wraps it in silken threads and, with the present held in his fangs (chelicerae), he goes looking for a bride. During courtship he gives his treat to the female. As soon as she begins to feast on it, the male can dare to approach her more closely and eventually copulate with her.

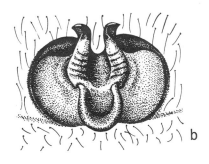

The male copulatory organ, the pedipalpus (a), and the female genital opening covered with a sculptured plate (epigyne) (b) in an orb-weaver spider *Araneus umbraticus*.

cleverly covers the entrance to a pair of seminal receptacles, called spermathecae, that may also themselves form an intricate maze. The whole structure is a kind of complex species-specific lock.

Of course each lock has its own key. The adult male actually has two 'keys', both found at the end of the pedipalpi (a pair of small leg-like appendages between the chelicerae and the first pair of legs). The end segment of each pedipalpus is transformed into a combination of a temporary sperm reservoir and a secondary copulatory organ. The pedipalpi thus resemble hands wearing boxing gloves. The dorsal side of the last segment is hairy, carrying tactile and chemical receptors. The palm side of the 'glove' is bare and intricately sculptured, resembling the female's epigyne. Arachnologists call it the bulbus. The sperm reservoir has a thorn-like outlet called an embolus. During copulation, the bulbus finds its counterpart in the female's epigyne, and the embolus is aimed so that the sperm will enter one of the spermathecae.

The male has to make special preparations before setting off on his hazardous mission. He spins a small triangular net, no larger than half his body size and releases a droplet of sperm onto it from his genital opening. In order to ejaculate, he stimulates himself by rubbing his underbelly against the rim of the net. Then he draws the droplet into his sperm reservoir in the bulbus, rather like filling a fountain pen.

Many of the spider species make use of specific scents as love potions. In web-building spiders, the female wafts airborne pheromones to lure the male, who is guided by the smell from as far away as a metre. In the wandering species, the female makes a scented trail on a dragline which she leaves behind wherever she goes. The male follows the line, touching the silk with the sensory hairs on his pedipalpi.

During the later, more intimate phases of courtship the other senses take on a greater role. As we already know, the male of jumping spiders tries to woo his partner by displaying his beauty and performing specific signalling gestures with his

109

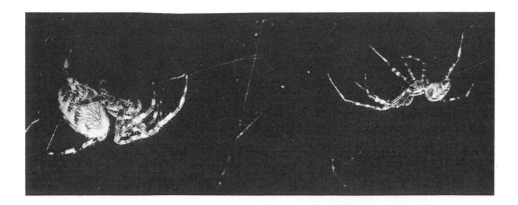

legs. The majority of spiders, however, have poor eyesight, and they express their intentions with sounds instead of movements. Despite the fact that nobody has ever heard a spider sing, they are unmatched by any group of animals (with the possible exception of insects) in their possession of a rich array of acoustic-vibratory means of communication.

Airborne sounds are perceived by spiders with their trichobothria, i.e. the long fine hairs on their legs. Vibrations that travel beneath their feet are picked up by special slit sense organs which are scattered all over the body, most of them being located near the joints of their extremities.

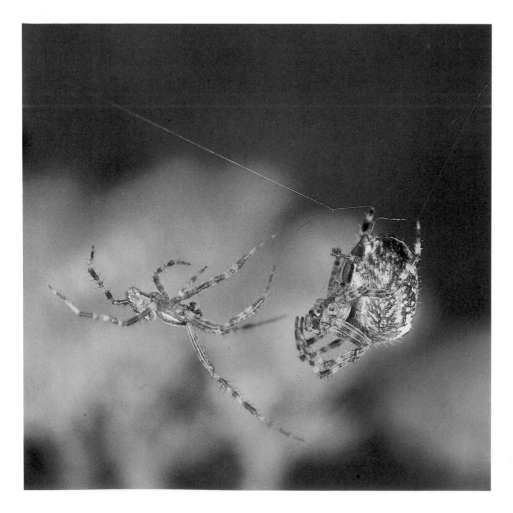

In spite of being cautious, the male garden spider (*Araneus diadematus*) ended his amorous adventure in the fangs of his bride. In the last picture of the series he can already be seen as a prey wrapped in the silk.

Web-building spiders send messages along their silk lines. A courting male produces specific signals on the threads of the female's net by various means. He plucks, drums or stridulates with file and washboard-type organs, similar to those of many insects. The female usually responds by twanging the web or pulling individual lines, undoubtedly according to some species-specific code. In some orb-weavers (Araneidae), the male takes special preparations by attaching his own 'mating line' to the female's web. By plucking at it, he notifies the female of his presence and his intentions. Generally the female answers by crossing from her web to his mating line and moving toward the wooer. He easily determines her intentions according to the speed at which she approaches. If she rushes too eagerly toward him, he stops signalling and beats a hasty retreat or simply cuts off her access line. After a while, he repeats his approach. If he attempts this manoeuvre several times in succession, her predatory drive gradually becomes exhausted. The males of two orb-weaver species have even improved this safety measure. The suitor connects the mating line directly with the outlet of his spinnerets, which enables him to produce a virtually endless line. He can thus give his dangerous partner all the rope she needs to work out her aggression before he lets her come close.

Many spiders that do not build webs produce sounds by drumming on various objects. In the wolf spiders (Lycosidae), the substrate-born vibrations are even more important for communication than the visual signals mentioned earlier. They

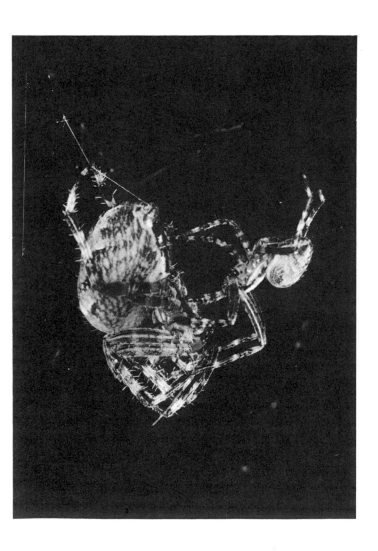

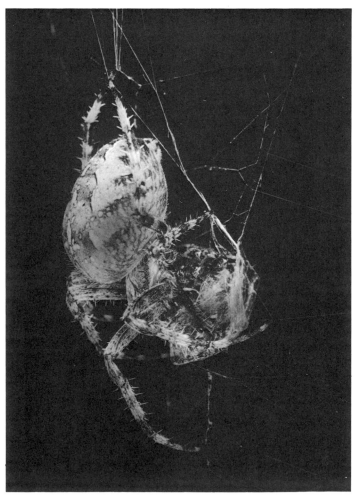

beat on leaves with their pedipalpi, and some may also emit a faintly audible purring sound produced by a stridulatory organ on their pedipalpi.

Another arachnid trick is one practised by large tropical spiders that are occasionally imported in bunches of bananas. The male banana spider (*Heteropoda venatoria*) fastens himself by means of special tarsal hairs to a resonant surface such as a banana leaf. By vibrating his whole body he gives off pulsed low-frequency signals (around 50 Hz), which are barely audible to us but which travel surprisingly well along the plant. In the nocturnal wandering spider of the family Ctenidae, *Cupienius salei,* the male 'talks' with the female from a distance of up to one metre. The male begins sending his vibratory signals on detecting the female's sex pheromone. Thick leaf-stalks will carry his message to the female, who may be hidden in a different part of the plant. Her responses are the only guide for the male in his search for a mate.

The patience required for seeing how spiders start a family will be well-rewarded. There is a tinge of comedy in the male spider's method of transferring his sperm. He inserts the thorn-like embolus of his copulatory organ into the female's epigyne. At each ejaculation, all the spines on his body stand on edge. Each species has its own variation in details. Quite often the male climbs onto the female's back, perhaps to avoid her dangerous fangs. In some tiny species of the dwarf spiders (Erigonidae), which copulate in the 'face-to-face' position, the male has complex knobs on the front of his cephalothorax, into which the female bites during the act. The knobs are glandular formations producing secretions presumably inhibiting her from turning her love bites into devourment. Males of long-jawed orb-weavers (Tetragnathidae) have another approach: they 'take the bull by the horns'. Their giant fangs are provided with spines and spurs, into which the fearsome jaws of the female are locked before copulation. In some small crab spiders (Thomisidae) the courting male clamps onto one of the legs of his partner, and she, instead of attacking him, runs off dragging the male behind her. Their amorous skirmish ends with the male climbing onto his spouse's back. There he caresses her to calm her

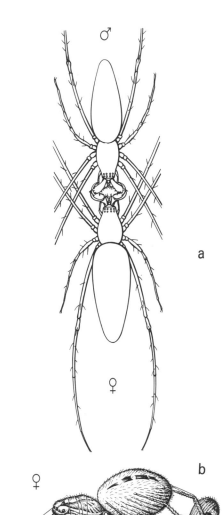

It is obvious from these pictures how the males of the long-jawed orb-weaver (*Tetragnatha*) (a) and of the crab spider (*Xysticus*) (b) secure themselves before copulation.

The males of the crab spiders *Misumena vatia* and *Thomisus albus* look like dwarves next to their plump females (at left). They too often do not survive their nuptial night (top right).

down so he can later slip underneath her large belly without great risk. The male *Xysticus viaticus* of the same family fondles his partner for some time with the ulterior motive of tying her to the ground with silk threads. When the copulation is over, it takes the female a while to extricate herself from the bondage. Meantime, the male makes his getaway.

Quite a range of other tricks have been evolved by male spiders to help them make a fast and safe retreat after copulation. Some wolf spiders pinch the female with their venomous chelicerae, temporarily and harmlessly paralyzing her. The male orb-weavers use several methods of emergency escape. In the simplest case, the male merely bails out, taking advantage of gravity to reach safe ground. Others prepare a post-copulatory escape in advance by stretching out an elastic thread. When the mating is over, they literally catapult themselves away from danger. Despite all these devious inventions, some males still pay with their lives for their mating act. Thus their curious love-making confers on their young not only the genes of their sexual cells, but also the very proteins from their own bodies.

Similar strife occurs in other animal groups. The mantids (Mantodea) are an infamous example of cannibalism. The female habitually mistakes her suitor for prey, and before he can act further, she has eaten his head. A bizarre turn of events may follow. The rest of the male's body usually escapes (temporarily) from the female's jaws and begins a macabre dance around his attacker. Circling her body,

This photodocumentary about the tragic love of the male praying mantis (*Mantis religiosa*) needs no comment.

he dodges out of range of her mandibles and zeroes in on the more desirable features, at the tip of her abdomen, with admirable dexterity. His headless torso makes its way onto her back and, as if realizing the impending finale, he intensifies his movements to complete the pre-mortal act.

The explanation is simple. By eating the male's head, the female destroys his subaesophageal nerve ganglion, which normally inhibits the activity of the nerve centres in his abdomen, which in turn control the copulatory movements of the genitals. The abdomen frenziedly makes up for lost time when it is no longer fettered by the head's control. Even though not all mantid affairs end so tragically, the headless lover demonstrates to us that he is inherently adapted to the barbarous habits of his mate. Scientists have learned to take advantage of this phenomenon when breeding mantids degenerated by a prolonged stay in the laboratory. Males in such breeding stocks do not readily mate. However, this can usually be rectified by clipping off the male's head and placing him on the female's back.

Some orchids have made jilted lovers out of males of several hymenopterous species. These aristocratic plants use hymenopterans to serve them as pollinators and, unlike other herbs, make no attempt to give anything in return. The delusive blossoms of bee-orchids of the genus *Ophris* represent the craftiest guile ever set for an insect. From their fragrant glands — osmophores — the flowers emit volatile compounds resembling the female sex pheromones of some solitary bees and other hymenopterans. As we know, these compounds act on males as irresistible attractants and aphrodisiacs. When the male detects the fragrance, he will single-mindedly follow it to its source. The appearance of the blossom will not arouse his suspicions, for it closely resembles the form of a female wasp, complete with eyes, antennae and wings. When the male lands on the hairy surface of the petal, the deception is completed, for even his sense of touch will not alert him. The fervour of the thrice-deceived male then culminates in an attempt at copulation with the orchid. As he does so, he deposits a load of pollen within the orchid flower and immediately afterwards receives a fresh batch to carry to the next false female. A long time ago, the bee-orchids were given names to reflect the fidelity of their mimicry of particular insects. These flowers all look like a female insect resting on another simple blossom. It is no wonder they attracted the attention of botanists back in the days of Linnaeus. Their scientific names such as *Ophris insectifera, apifera, bombyliflora, tenthredinifera* or *sphecodes* are the best evidence that the naturalists realized the connection of certain orchids with particular insects.

The blossoms of this rare orchid, *Ophris fucifera,* are pollinated by the males of the solitary wasp of the genus *Eucera* (left).

However, the biological function of these peculiarly shaped flowers was then a subject of guesswork. More than two centuries passed before scientists found proof that the real function of the deceitful blossoms transcended the most daring imaginings of the old botanists.

The first observations, more than 50 years ago, of hymenopterous males' nuptial visits to bee-orchid flowers excited the entire world's scientific population. These findings provoked stormy discussions about the correctness of interpretations of the observed behaviour. The conclusions seemed too fantastic to be true. It was only two decades ago, after Swedish scientists led by Professor Bertil Kullenberg of Uppsala University had obtained evidence about the chemical nature of the attractants in bee-orchid fragrances, that the dispute ended. The Swedish scientists isolated, identified and analyzed compounds both from the orchids and from the insects that sexually stimulate male hymenopterans. By comparing the chemical structure of the extracts, they confirmed the similarity and, in some cases, the equivalence of many components from the two radically different sources. They also discovered that each bee-orchid species has its own attractant, by which the flowers can lure only certain wasp species.

The blossoms of these orchids often open before hymenopterous females have emerged and become sexually mature. It seems, though, that female insects do not suffer undue competition from wily blossoms: their males were observed to service both females of their own kind and the fraudulent flowers. Cases have been recorded, however, that indicate that the plant fragrances are even more effective on the male than is the authentic pheromone of the female.

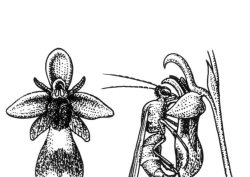

The delusive blossoms of the *Ophris* orchids may seduce males of some hymenopterous species so that they copulate with them. Such an act is called pseudocopulation, and it can occur because the flowers resemble and, more importantly, smell like the female (right).

TAKING CARE OF THE BROOD

The breeding season culminates in the caring for the young. There are some parents in the animal world that do not take much, if any, care of their offspring. These animals have to make up for the consequent losses by producing large numbers of eggs. In most insects, the maternal duties of each female begin and end with selecting a suitable place to lay her eggs, somewhere where the freshly hatched larvae will have food 'right under their noses'. However, there are quite a few exemplary mothers even among the insects and related arthropods, who increase the survival rate of their brood by caring for it, carrying, guarding and perhaps feeding it. In mammals and nidifugous birds, the care of the young is exclusively the business of the mother. There are, however, a few animals in which only the fathers are responsible for the young once they are born or hatched. Careful and nurturing fathers can be found among the marine worms polychaetes, in pycnogonids, frogs, some fish and birds, and rarely also in insects. In monogamous species, both parents participate in raising the family.

In any case, a prerequisite for a successful parent-child relationship is their ability to communicate in a variety of situations. It is imperative for both generations not only to be able to recognize one another, but also to understand each other during feeding or when danger approaches.

A female mallard (*Anas platyrhynchos*) with her young.

TALKING WITH THE EGG

Recognition within the family

In Nature the first living thing freshly hatched ducklings see is their mother. If one leaves a duckling during the critical period (between the 8th and 20th hour of its life) in the presence of any moving object, the duckling will follow it as if it were its own mother, and will remember it for the rest of its life.

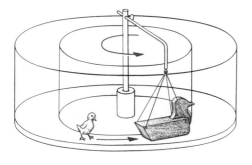

How do the young manage to recognize their mother? Is this ability innate? Or must they memorize their mother's looks? A century ago, D. Spalding discovered that orphaned chicks which are only two or three days old will follow any moving object. Half a century later, an Austrian ethologist, Konrad Lorenz, studied this phenomenon in great detail among water fowl, particularly ducks. Professor Lorenz concluded that during the first hours after hatching, a unique process of learning takes place in the ducklings, chicks and other nidifugous birds. The young learn unbelievably fast and permanently to recognize their parent and to imprint her characteristic traits on their memory. The phenomenon is therefore known as imprinting. The most surprising feature of this ability to learn is the fact that a permanent bond with a 'dummy mother' can easily be formed. The surrogate mother might be almost anything: a human, a balloon, a blinking light, a toy or even a match box. If such an object is made to move in the vicinity of a fledgling during the sensitive period of its early life, the young bird will steadfastly follow it and resist any persuasion to do otherwise. A pairing with sound stimuli from the moving object, whatever it may be, will make the imprinting even stronger.

The critical period for imprinting in a duckling's life occurs between its eighth and twentieth hour. A duckling can learn the features of a dummy and feel impelled to follow it after a mere one-minute exposure to this false parent.

Young wood ducks, nesting in tree hollows, hear their mother's call from the water before they can see her. This led to the evolution of auditory imprinting in these birds. The little drakes also learn what their future mate should look like from their own mother's example. If the ducklings of any species are experimentally raised in the presence of a drake, the male offspring will become homosexual. Birds raised by man encounter similar problems in their adulthood. A falconist's head has been known to become the object of sexual desire for a captive bird of prey whose only concept of mother was his human master.

Young mice and rats also learn what to look for in a mate, but they choose by smell more than by appearance. When infant female mice were reared by parents

120

repeatedly sprayed by a perfume, when reaching adulthood they sought out males scented with this particular perfume in preference to unscented males. This clearly demonstrates that young female mice in the laboratory are imprinted with the smell of their father. If the young mouse has no opportunity to smell him, or if the male's smell is suppressed by a deodorant, the deprived daughter will have trouble in discriminating between sexes as an adult. In another experiment, young male rats were reared by mothers whose nipples and vagina were daily sprayed with lemon scent. On reaching adulthood, each male was introduced into a cage with a lemon-scented or an unscented female rat. It turned out that sons of lemon-scented mothers mounted more readily and ejaculated more quickly with lemon-scented sex partners than unscented ones, while sons of unscented mothers preferred unscented females. Another type of olfactory bond was discovered in laboratory rats. The faeces of lactating mothers are irresistible to the newborn due to volatile compounds known as the maternal pheromone; the young rats eagerly eat their mother's droppings. Later studies showed that the faeces contain certain compounds which protect the young against gut infections and stimulate development of the brain. The maternal pheromone also helps the wandering litter-mates to find their way back home. The father also contributes a great deal to family unity, at least in mice. A chemical called the paternal pheromone, contained in his urine, significantly suppresses the mobility of his offspring, thus discouraging them from roaming.

Even an animal as shy as the hare (*Lepus europaeus*) may lose the fear of man if it has been hand raised by people.

121

The exchange of acoustic signals in nidicolous birds starts well before hatching. The embryos communicate among themselves by peeping, making a 'collective decision' about the time of hatching. The more advanced nestmates literally 'egg on' the belated ones, and lagging ones in turn urge the front runners to slow down the pace of development a bit by their calls. As a result, the whole batch hatches simultaneously. The last hatchling of the European coot (*Fulica atra*) will not keep the others waiting more than a few minutes for its exit from the egg.

The first sounds uttered by the piping bird embryo are listened to attentively by the sitting mother. If duck eggs are put under a pheasant hen, the hen will incubate them as her own until the ducklings give themselves away by starting to vocalize. When the hen realizes the deception, she smashes the shells and may even kill the young ducks. A nesting duck who has had her eggs replaced by those of another species also recognizes that the voices she hears are not from her own offspring but remains on the nest, even after her foster children are hatched and running around. The female goshawk (*Accipiter gentilis*) incubates a duck's egg with alacrity, and when the young duck has hatched, she will even attempt to feed it. All is not as well as it seems, however. As soon as the duckling tries to leave the nest, the foster mother will attack it as if it were prey. Only the tame barnyard hen can be duped into incubating and bringing up ducklings or goslings without repercussion, due to the centuries of domestication which have blunted her instincts.

The sitting hen not only understands the voices that issue from within the eggs, she also replies to them. Her chicks learn, while still in the shell, to recognize the sounds of their parent through an exchange of acoustic signals. Thus prepared, they can distinguish parental calls from those of other birds immediately after hatching. Reciprocal recognition of individual family members is particularly important in birds that regularly nest in dense colonies. Gulls, terns, gannets, oystercatchers, auks and penguins can recognize their own offspring among hoards of other youngsters. Gull chicks are already busy vocalizing three days before emerging from the shell. This gives their mother plenty of time to pinpoint their vocal idiosyncrasies.

122

The variety of sounds coming from the unhatched domestic chick may be surprisingly rich. All kinds of cheeping, twittering or screeching can be heard from the egg a day prior to the chick's entry into the world. As a matter of fact, a sonographic analysis has disclosed seven different calls. Four of them resemble the distress cries of a hatched chicken, and three may be called pleasure calls. When the mother hears a distress call, she stands up, ruffles her feathers and gives a soothing cluck. The becalmed chick either falls silent or answers with a pleasure call.

Conversation between the hen and her brood becomes even more involved after hatching. The chick has three basic calls. The cry of desolation is given off whenever the chick loses sight of its mother. It is a loud and piercing sound, for which the ears of the hen are most sensitive. The lost chick will call until completely exhausted, because it cannot survive without the protection and warmth of its mother's body. Another important signal a young chick makes is the huddle call, which says 'I'm here. Where are you?' The young one expects an answer from its mother or nest mates. If no reply is received, it immediately lets loose a call of desolation, even if it is resting securely beneath its mother's wings. The third message that may be given is one of sleepiness. It is a request to take a nap in the warmth of the hen's body.

Mammalian mothers and their progeny also rely on voice as one means of communication. We are familiar with the voices of puppies, kittens, kids, calves and foals. Some animals, however, do not communicate on our wavelength; we will never hear the voices of young bats, or of mice, rats and other rodents, because these creatures use ultrasound to impart their indignation at various unpleasant sensations. Carefully designed experiments showed that the female sheep

A pair of microphones (m) and loudspeakers (a) mediated a conversation between a female duck sitting on the clutch of dummy eggs in her nest at the pond and the real eggs in the laboratory incubator. By means of this experiment the scientists learned and tape recorded (t) many details about the conversation that takes place between a mother and her young before hatching.

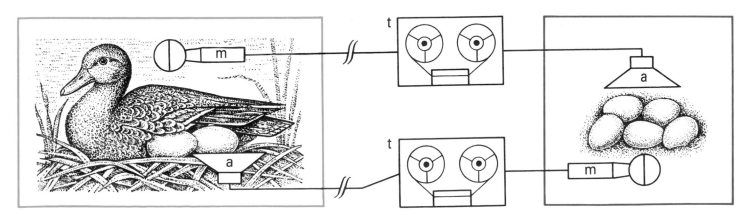

distinguishes the voice of her own lamb from the bleating of strange lambs, but she will allow it to suck only after she verifies its identity by scent. Smell is, after all, the most significant sense used by mammals to recognize their own offspring. In many species, olfactorial imprinting has been proven. One such case is the goat, who must sniff and lick her kid within an hour of its birth. If she is prevented from doing so, she will reject the kid later. A mere five-minute contact during the sensitive period is sufficient for preventing her from shunning it. If the goat is deprived of her sense of smell before parturition, she will accept any kid as her own later on.

Mouflons or deer recognize their own offspring by sniffing their anal and tail regions. If the young one is dressed up in panties, its mother will not recognize it. In the same manner, a bitch tolerates only her own puppies, killing any others that are added to the litter unless they are first perfumed with the smell of her den. In contrast, a male dog will foster any puppies, whether or not they are his progeny. There is a good reason for this. If the bitch loses her original partner, she may take up with another male to assist in raising her family.

An extraordinary ability to recognize one's own young has evolved among social animals living in large herds. Considering that a herd of harp seals (*Pagophilus groenlandicus*) may contain tens of thousands of members, it is something of a miracle that each mother can find her young when she returns from hunting in the sea. In the continuously changing environment of the breaking ice floes, she can hardly count on any visual cues. What remains available to her is her sense of hearing and smell. The searching seal mother is first guided by the voice of her pup, and then sniffs her young to confirm its identity.

The use of vocal cords comes into play even in the least expected of animals — the crocodiles. The female crocodile buries her eggs in the sand and may also cover them with a pile of vegetation. When the time of hatching approaches, the egg-encased crocodiles begin to call. Their peeping is loud enough to be heard several metres away, despite the eggshell, sand and vegetation sound barriers. This hubbub is a signal for their mother to remove the sand and release the hatching youngsters. As the little crocodiles scramble out, the mother takes them gently in her powerful jaws and carries them in a special pouch on the bottom of her mouth to a secluded spot in the swamp, which will serve as a nursery for them. There they will reside, under the supervision of both parents, for several months.

A female mouflon (*Ovis musimon*) is one of the mammalian mothers that gets imprinted to the smell of its newborn.

In a similar way as the wolf (*Canis lupus*), many other carnivores and rodents transport their young in the mouth. The grip on the neck is a signal for the young to assume a relaxed and motionless position. Zoologists call it 'transportation catalepsis'.

IT'S HARD TO RAISE
A FAMILY

Signals for feeding
and warning

If you touch a blackbird's nest, thus simulating the landing of an adult bird, the nestlings will open their beaks and loudly beg for food (above).

The two most prominent manifestations of parental behaviour can be seen each spring in any farmyard. Just watch a hen leading her chicks around for a while. Although it is true that the domestic fowl does not directly feed her young, nonetheless during the first day of a chick's life she gives it guidance in finding food. When she spies a delicacy, she picks it up with her beak and drops it in an obvious way in front of her, calling to her chicks with a 'took, took' sound. Her young understand well what this means, having taken lessons while still in their shells. They come to her and peck at the offered food. If the hen senses a danger in the form of a dog, cat or strange hen, she will give off a warning cackle that will cause her chicks to take cover. Should the intruder come too close, the clucking hen may attack it.

An immense array of signals is used by animal parents for feeding or warning their family. Good examples can be found in the nidicolous birds, i.e. birds that feed their young in the nest. The newly hatched nestlings of songbirds are blind and therefore they obviously cannot recognize their parents by appearance. Instead they respond to the shaking of the nest and fanning of air caused by adult birds landing on the nest. They stretch their necks straight up and open their beaks, exposing the brightly coloured interior of their gullets, usually yellow, orange or red. Some weaver birds (Ploceidae) and cut-throats (*Amadina*) even have special light-reflecting warts lining the edge of the inside of their mouths. The eye-catching colours within a nestling's beak elicit the feeding response in the adult bird. As the growing youngsters open their eyes, they begin to respond to the silhouettes of their parents. However, they will even beg from a dummy that bears little resemblance to an adult bird. When shown an irregularly shaped disc, they will direct their beaks toward any projection or indentation on its perimeter. Apparently, they have an inborn generalized concept of the beak as a formation that provides food.

Nest parasites, such as the cuckoo (*Cuculus canorus*), take advantage of the blind instincts of small nidicolous birds. The female cuckoo looks for a nest with a fresh clutch of eggs and replaces one of the host eggs with an egg of her own. Her hawk-like shape may be an aid in this cunning behaviour. When the cuckoo approaches the chosen nest, the frightened nest owner flies away, giving the cuckoo plenty of time to make the switch; ten seconds is all that is needed to carry out the task. Since the cuckoo's young hatches in only twelve and a half days, it usually beats the host eggs' incubation time. During the first four days the parasitic nestling instinctively pushes everything out of the nest with which it comes in contact: the eggs or young of its foster parents, or any objects experimentally put into the nest. The young cuckoo has several characteristics which make it an 'ideal child'. The orange-red interior of its open beak is so inviting that even strange birds passing by may be charmed into feeding it.

When learning about the private lives of bird families, one may be astonished at the close co-operation of parental couples. In some species the male and female take turns in incubating the eggs. The 'changing of the guard' is generally accompanied by considerable ceremony, with special movements and calls.

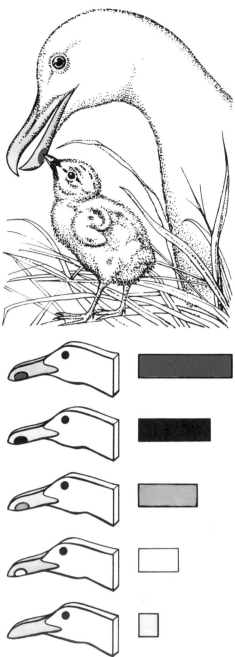

All gulls carry the food for their young in the crop and regurgitate it when asked by the chicks; a hungry young taps the parent's beak. The sign stimulus eliciting the begging response of young herring gulls (*Larus argentatus*) is the red spot on the lower jaw of an adult bird's beak. The experiments with various models have shown that the most important characteristics are the colour and the contrast of the spot, whereas the shape of the beak is less important. The chicks will tap even the red-painted nails of a human hand.

The black-headed gull (*Larus ridibundus*) feeding its young.

127

Contrary to popular belief, the sitting bird is not a long-suffering parent waiting wistfully to be relieved of nesting duties. The incubation instinct is often so strong that the bird on second shift has to push its partner forcefully off the nest. Birds use various signals when they want to take their turn. The woodpecker drums on a branch, while the flightless cormorant of the Galapagos Islands, *Nannopterus harissi,* brings a symbolic present of seaweed to his mate on the nest. The green sandpiper (*Tringa ochropus*), which nests in the trees of dense riverine woods, announces with a special call from afar that its turn has come. The sitting bird answers the call before leaving the nest. The approaching bird keeps up its call until assuming its place on the eggs. The off-duty bird then announces in which region of the nesting territory it will be foraging for food. When moving to another quarter, the roaming bird first returns to the nest to inform its spouse of the new location. The sitting bird acknowledges the message with a vocal response. Should the nest be raided by an intruder, the bird knows where to fly to get help.

During the first few days after their eggs have hatched the sandpiper parents have strictly divided duties. While one of them, usually the father, leads the chicks and teaches them to feed in the dense ground vegetation, the other partner assumes an elevated post to watch for enemies. If danger threatens, the parent on guard calls loudly to divert the enemy's attention to itself. Meanwhile, the young family is led away by the soft calls of its guiding parent to a safer place.

In many bird species, the warning call of the parents is an order to keep quiet. The field ornithologists who ring young wading birds are well acquainted with this instinct. As long as the chicks can hear the warning cries of their parent, they remain calmly in the hands of the bird ringer. If they get out of earshot of the adult bird, however, they flutter and squirm in alarm and are almost impossible to hold.

Birds of prey also divide parental duties in an arbitrary way. The male European sparrow-hawk (*Accipiter nisus*) helps the female build the nest and occasionally even sits on the eggs. Once the young are hatched, however, the father's exclusive duty is to supply the family with food. The female, in turn, is permanently on the nest feeding, warming or shading the fledglings. Later she needs only to guard the nest. The male cleans and plucks the prey in a special 'station' near the nest, after announcing his return from a successful hunt with a stereotyped call. The female usually responds to his voice by leaving the nest to pick up the prepared meal. If she

When the common tern (*Sterna hirundo*) parents take turns in sitting on the eggs, a short 'changing of the guards' ceremony can be seen.

does not come to collect it, the male delivers the food directly to the nest. However, should the female die, the male is unable to brind up the family on his own. He can supply the nest with plenty of provisions, but if the nestlings are too young to take the meat into their beaks by themselves and tear it into bite-size pieces, they will die of starvation while being literally buried under their meals.

The males of the marsh harrier (*Circus aeruginosus*) and Montagu's harrier (*C. pygargus*) have similar responsibilities also, being the sole suppliers of sustenance to their families. Some drama is added to the father's return from a good

A young cuckoo (*Cuculus canorus*) must sit on the nest of its foster parents, the great reed warblers (*Acrocephalus arundinaceus*), very quietly, in order to avoid falling through. Disciplined behaviour is inherited to the young cuckoos.

When the common kingfisher (*Alcedo atthis*) is just about to feed a fish to its young, it always holds the prey with the head sticking out of its beak.

The nestlings of the black-crowned night heron (*Nycticorax nycticorax*) will assault with their sharp beaks everybody who approaches their nest. Their own parents must, therefore, introduce themselves whenever they come to feed them. They do so by a deep bow thereby displaying their long, white feathers on top of the head.

hunt, however. He calls his partner as he approaches the nest, and she flies up to meet him in the air. When the birds pass, the male flies above the female and drops the prey. She deftly turns upside-down to catch it. Sometimes the predatory pair transfer the food from his talons to hers while still on the wing.

It is possible to find commendable parents among insects as well. The complex parental care of the carrion beetles (*Nicrophorus*) is well known among entomologists. If one beetle finds a fresh cadaver of, say, a mouse, it calls its partner by means of a pheromone. Together they bury the precious find in the soil. Then they make an underground chamber for the corpse, which is reconstituted into a big meaty ball. The process of decomposition of the proteinaceous matter in this bolus is controlled by the beetles' salivary secretions. In the meantime, the female lays her eggs in a small side chamber. The larvae hatch just as the food becomes liquefied. The mother guides the freshly hatched young to the liquid proteins by stridulating. She takes the food into her mouth and feeds the larvae mouth to mouth, one by one until all are nourished. Sometimes the father also assists in feeding them.

130

In the family of the honey buzzard (*Pernis apivorus*) the parental duties are divided almost equally between the partners. The male participates in building the nest and incubating the eggs, helps to shade the hatchlings and feeds them as expertly as the female. The female reciprocates by helping to hunt for food.

At least for the first few days of their brand new existence, spider young are cared for by their mother. Almost all spiders deposit their eggs in cocoons which are fastened in a protected place, or carried around by the female, as in the case of wolf spiders (Lycosidae). The mother wolf spider can tell when the young are hatching by the vibrations inside the cocoon. She tears it open and lets the spiderlings crawl onto her abdomen, where they will cling to special knob-like hairs. When the

In the European sparrowhawk (*Accipiter nisus*) (left) only the mother cares for and feeds the young. The considerably smaller father hunts and stocks the nest. Similarly, in the northern goshawk (*Accipiter gentilis*) only females can feed their young (right).

mother is not walking around, the little spiders can climb down to the ground and wander around or drink water. They remain, however, in constant contact with the hairs on her abdomen through the slender draglines of silk. If disturbed, the mother calls her young back by erecting the abdominal hairs and pulling at their draglines. The mother spider's predatory instincts and cannibalistic tendencies are suppressed as long as she carries her offspring with her.

Some female web-building spiders also communicate with their young, who share the family web for a certain length of time after hatching. If the female of a combfooted spider *Theridium saxatile* catches prey in the web, she warns her youngsters with a shake of the web to take cover until the still-living meal is subdued. The spiderlings hide in a safe corner of the web until their mother calls them with another vibratory signal. She regurgitates the half-digested food when they demand it by tapping at her forelegs. The young gather around their mother and form almost a straight line waiting for feeding. They take turns making contact with the mother, two or three sucking at a time. This mouth-to-mouth feeding is a common scene in many spider nurseries.

Spiderlings of a common European funnel weaver, *Coelotes terrestris*, stay with their mother for as long as two months. At first they are fed by regurgitation, later they also beg for prey caught by the mother. After she sizes an insect, she communicates with her offspring by making special movements, summoning the spiderlings to share the food. When they come and solicit by touching her jaws, she releases the prey and lets them to feed on it. As a warning signal, she stamps her fourth leg, and the young scurry into hiding. The mother can distinguish between her young and potential prey by the differences in vibrations in the web and by touch. After the mother's death in autumn, the spiderlings suck her body fluids. Only later they leave the family nest to establish their own solitary webs.

Communication between members of different generations is particularly well developed in spiders living together in communal nests, as exemplified by an eresid spider, *Stegodyphus sarasinorum*. Tho colony of this social spider may contain 500 to 900 members. Their web is made of very viscous silk so that even powerful insects cannot escape once they strike it. Indeed, the prey is usually much larger

Current studies indicate that the nutritive material is not simply stored food, but is the product of secretion from gut cells that is then released through the mouth.

The scorpions also belong to those invertebrate groups in which the female carries the young on her back for a certain time after hatching.

A female *Pardosa lugubris,* similarly as the females of other wolf spiders (Lycosidae), carries first a cocoon with the eggs and later spiderlings wherever she goes.

Parental care is well known in some bugs (Heteroptera). A female of a pentatomid bug, *Elasmucha betulae,* guards both her eggs and later the hatchlings on the underside of a birch leaf. She protects them from parasitic insects and moulds. Her maternal instinct is so strong that she will not desert her offspring even if the leaf falls down and dries out. The tie between mother and young is probably of a chemical nature.

than the spiders. Whenever an insect is caught, the hordes of spiders stream out, encircle the prey, and carry it back inside the nest, where they communally suck it out. Females attach their egg cases to the walls of the nest and guard them zealously. In laboratory experiments females took turns guarding the cocoons. If the colony is invaded by an ant swarm, the spiders leave the nest, and often females take their egg cases with them. Freshly hatched spiderlings do not feed at first but cluster around the mother. Only later are they fed by her mouth-to-mouth. Most interestingly, females tolerate and feed spiderlings in the colony that are not necessarily their own. The radioisotopes fed to one marked female appeared not only in her young, but also in the offspring of another, unlabelled female. In this way communal brood care has been for the first time conclusively demonstrated in a spider species.

133

ESTABLISHING SOCIAL POSITION

The word 'social' can be interpreted in several ways. When dealing with the relationships among animals, one of its meanings must be avoided: the term must be devoid of any judgemental tones, either negative or positive which we normally apply when speaking of human relations. In animals one should label as social even those phenomena which are considered 'asocial' if they occur in human society. This includes behaviour considered by our standards as selfish, rude, ruthless, brutal or even murderous. In animals these manifestations are a part of normal behaviour, since they serve the survival of the species best under the given circumstances. At the other end of the spectrum, altruistic actions of individual members should not cause us to heave a sentimental sigh in awe of the nobility of an animal's soul, since such behaviour follows the laws of Nature, which have as their ultimate goal the reproduction of genes. All animal martyrs share a common interest with other members of their species' society. Self-sacrifice is not an accurate term in this case, for it is their own genes that they save by dying.

An ethologist usually labels as social any relationships between members of a given species, i.e. the behaviour used for intraspecific communication. However, some authors use the term social in a narrower sense, limiting it to behaviour associated with the life within a group, such as a family, pack, herd or colony. The following chapters will be devoted to the vocabulary of animals which, having mastered a complex language, are able to live in well-organized societies.

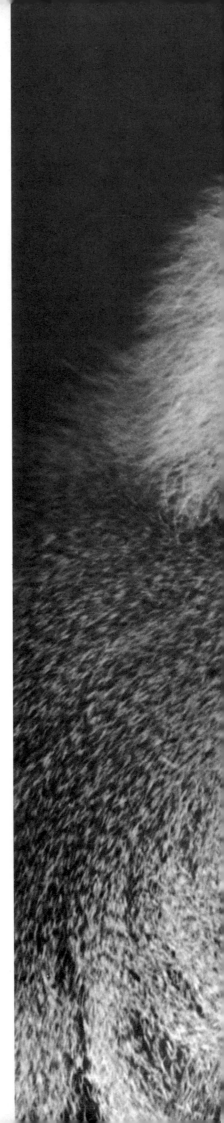

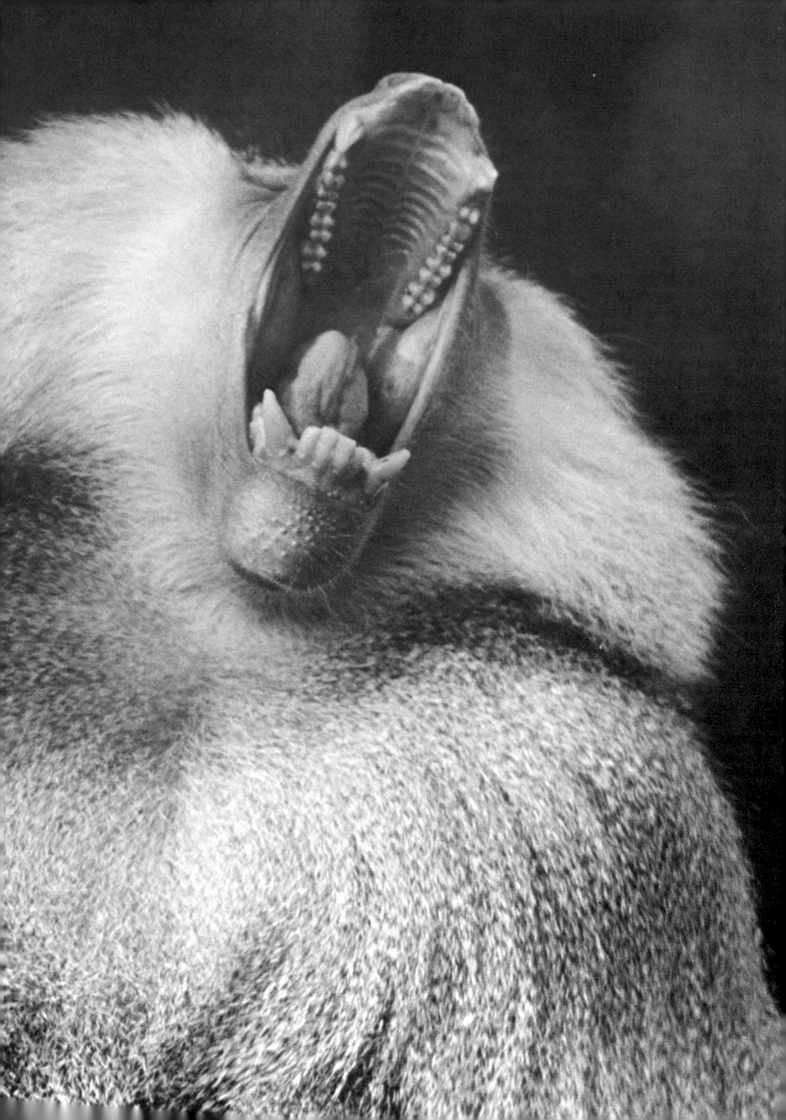

The controversial subject of intraspecific fighting is a complex one which incorporates the processes of courtship, mate selection and other social relationships among animals. It concerns any situation in which an animal has to compare its strength and abilities with those of another individual of its own species, be it for winning a better territory, more mates, or a higher social position.

A duel with a rival of one's own species usually has a different set of regulations than a fight with a predator or prey. The powerful weapons that normally serve for killing or defence are not generally employed. As a rule, the more dangerous the teeth, claws or beak, the stronger the inhibitions from using them. That is why the 'bloodthirsty' beasts of prey are much less aggressive toward each other than the 'peace-loving' herbivores.

In the initial phases of a confrontation, rivals compare their strength with harmless signals, often without even touching one another. Each makes all kinds of threats to the other in an attempt to intimidate and drive away the opponent. Only when all factors seem equal will the conflict escalate into a real fight. Even then, lethal weapons are not used. That would be detrimental to the species as a whole, injuring and weakening the population of fighters. That is not the objective of jousting. Therefore the behaviour of the contestants is ritualized, composed of fixed behavioural sequences that follow certain 'rules'. A weaker individual can withdraw and admit its defeat with an appeasement gesture. The loser usually turns away its weapons and exposes vulnerable parts of its body such as the belly or neck. This action is invariably a signal for the victor to halt its attack and allow the defeated one to clear out. In some species, the animals may have a bit of insurance against a quarrelsome adversary. The teeth of a male hippo or a sea lion can rarely penetrate the thick layer of fat beneath the skin of an opponent. Likewise, a lion's heavy mane makes a discouraging mouthful for a pugnacious foe.

Not all animal jousting is such a spectacular event as the one shown above in the illustrations of turkeys. When watching two animals squaring up, one often gets the impression that the fight is more of a game, in which the champion is the one who is the stronger and more skilful fighter.

Giraffes have short blunt horns, inadequate for fencing. Instead, they beat each other with their long necks. The attacking individual stands with his legs spread out and delivers a blow to the opponent's flank. The blow is returned in kind, and the

ANIMAL JOUSTING

Intraspecific fight rituals

The bare red skin on the head of a turkey is surprisingly thick and elastic. The purpose of this 'rubber helmet' can best be appreciated when viewing an encounter of two enraged males. Their skulls are well protected against the strong blows of the beak or claws during a duel.

contest is a grotesque pageant, done almost in slow motion as each deliberately takes his turn and then awaits the retort. With each thrust, the male attempts to bring his sparring partner to his knees. They play 'according to Hoyle' and never use their deadliest weapon — their hoofs. A giraffe can crush a lion's skull with a blow of its hoof, or splinter a four-centimetre thick wooden plank.

Everyone knows that the ram is true to his name when he wishes to prove how tough he is. In the duel, the rivals dash toward each other from a distance of some 20–30 metres and ram full speed into each other's curved horns in a head-on collision. Only the thickened frontal bone of their skulls keeps them from cracking each other's head open.

Equally famous are the deer, whose jousting involves opponents standing against each other with antlers locked together. They push and shove in an attempt to get the other down on his knees. There is no chivalry and a shocking number of males die in these battles. Some succumb because they cannot untangle their antlers and

The gemsboks (*Oryx gazella*) are great fencers. The males have long pointed horns, but never use them to impale an opponent of their own species. The contenders use their 'swords' as gentlemanly foils, barely making a touche. At full tilt, the most they will do to each other is to give a rough push with their foreheads. These antelopes may on occasion be seen demonstrating their prowess at the zoo.

starve to death, but more often their fatalities occur due to deep stab wounds, evidently inflicted by antlers.

An aquarium stocked with cichlid fish may offer the opportunity to witness still another type of jousting. Males push against each other with their mouths wide open or tug at each other with their jaws locked into one another. A thick layer of hardened skin protects their lips against serious injury. During this ritual fight, the fish abide by rules, which forbid an attack on the rival's vulnerable flanks or belly.

It is certainly a lesser known fact that snakes go in accordance to gentlemen's rules for duelling. Poisonous species such as the rattlesnake or viper would never use their deadly venom in matching strength, since they themselves are not immune to the poison's effects. The fighting males stretch up against each other with the first third of their bodies erect, pushing and thrashing each other with their heads. The showdown often looks more like a dance, since the snakes intertwine and sway their raised bodies from side to side. The aim is to exhaust the opponent and to press his weary body to the ground with a loop of the victor's own body. The defeated snake will crawl away without being seriously harmed.

It was demonstrated by a laboratory experiment with crickets that stridulation can serve as an effective weapon in the ritualized encounters of the territorial males. The house cricket (*Achaeta domesticus*) was the subject of study for entomologists at Pennsylvania State University. I have repeated the experiment using the two-spotted cricket (*Gryllus bimaculatus*) and got similar results. A championship was staged with ten participants; each male cricket was allowed to fight with every other male and a score was kept of the results of individual encounters. The three least successful fighters were deafened by piercing their ear drums (which are located on their forelegs) and were sent in for a rematch with the top three contenders. In most of the rounds, the latter did not defend their positions. There is only one explanation: by not being able to hear the virile sounds of their challengers, the weaker males did not know enough to be afraid. In their case, ignorance was bliss.

The ritualized tournaments of the honeypot ants (*Myrmecocystus mimicus*) reach nearly epic proportions. These ants owe their name to the fact that some workers are preferentially fed by the others until their abdomens swell into a grotesque globe. Barely able to move, they remain in the nest as living honeypots. The Australian aborigines love to eat them as sweets. The honeypot ants are merciless predators, feeding predominantly on termites. Their territory is not firmly delineated but varies conveniently to encompass new areas containing food in a kind of 'manifest destiny' policy. When the scout ants find a bonanza on one of their habitual long excursions, they lay a fragrant trail to guide the others toward it. The colony then defends this resource area as its territory until the food supply is depleted. If it discovers another colony of ants of the same species near the food source, it must do something to distract the attention of these potential competitors away from the edibles. Some of the scouts race home to recruit an army of maybe several hundred worker ants and lead them to the strangers' nest. The recruited ants surround the nest and engage all the workers that emerge from it in elaborated display tournaments. This keeps the other ants too busy to interfere and clears the way for food gathering to continue without disturbance from interlopers. Some scout ants may occasionally leave the battlefield in order to bring in reinforcements, but the tournament will not end until the harvest is safely gathered in.

Even though hundreds of honey pot worker ants participate in the territorial tournaments, no body-to-body combat occurs during the fight. Instead, individual ants engage in a highly stereotyped aggressive display (see the drawings at the

Fighting males of the common European viper (*Vipera berus*) try to push each other to the ground with the raised front parts of their body.

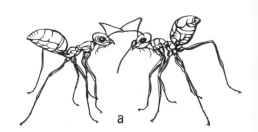

a

138

bottom of these two pages). The displaying ant walks on stilted legs with its head and abdomen raised. When accosting each other for the first time, they stand face to face (a), later standing side by side, elevating their abdomens still higher and tilting them toward the opponent (b). Simultaneously, they tap on each other's abdomen with their antennae. This is the only physical contact they make, except for attempting to nudge each other sideways. One of the fighters usually yields after 10 to 30 seconds. If the ant meets a member of its own colony, they greet each other with a short jerking display.

Ritualized fights can also take place among insects. If two male crickets get into a territorial dispute, each immediately tries to make the other back down by giving off a loud, intimidating chirping. This by itself may do the trick. However, when the two crickets find themselves in an equally matched vocal duel, they will attack each other with their mandibles. The body-to-body combat lasts only a few seconds, until the weaker fighter gives up. The winner sends him away with a triumph song.

b

There is more than one purpose for the tournaments. Besides keeping the competitors absorbed in battle during food gathering endeavours, it serves to assess the strength of their adversaries. If one of the colonies is much stronger than the other, that is, if it can gather many more contestants, the tournaments are soon over and the weaker colony is plundered. The queen is killed or expelled and the brood and honeypots are abducted to the victors' nest, where they are incorporated. This is the first known case of slavery (dulosis) among members of the same ant species.

The main means of communication within and between the armies of the six-legged fighters are fragrances. Chemical trails are laid by the scout ants for the others to follow; other more volatile scent signals are released to alarm nestmates and to recruit aid; the home odour identifies individual nestmates when they meet on the battlefield; and the smell of strangers induces aggressive display in participants of the expedition.

It is hoped that the reader has been convinced with this chapter that intraspecific fights may not be so cruel and bloody as is generally believed. All of the inhibitory mechanisms and rituals mentioned here and all of the special body adaptations undoubtedly belong among the greatest evolutionary achievements in Nature. On the one hand, they allow an animal to refine and maintain its fighting skills to the utmost and to advertize its abilities without inhibition while defending its territory, competing for a mate or struggling for a position within the group. On the other hand, the strict rules of the jousting ceremonies usually prevent the fight from going too far and ending tragically. This all supports the conclusion that the purpose of intraspecific aggression is to displace rather then to kill a rival. Until recently, an

The 'antlers' of the giant stag beetle (*Lucanus cervus*) are the greatly enlarged mandibles and they occur only in males. The photographs of two fighting beetles show how useful they are in the wrestling contest.

opinion prevailed among ethologists that killing among members of the same species was a rare phenomenon. However, reports from the wild on fatal intraspecific conflicts are increasing. Fights that ended in death have been recounted in lions, hyenas, some ruminants, various rodents, and among birds such as gulls or divers. In most of these cases, the animals lived in groups and the victims were usually strangers. Views on the function of such aggressive encounters in these species have to be revised. The rules of ritualized contests are apparently respected only within members of a clan. Under specific circumstances, such as overcrowding, the biological function of the intraspecific aggression may indeed be a regulation of the population density.

141

A surprisingly large number of animal species have developed social organizations, irrespective of the degree of evolution they have reached. Under certain ecological conditions, living together proved to be an advantage, increasing the chance of survival of individual members of the group. Banding together is a boon to defence, hunting for food, caring for the brood or for building complex communal homes. Life in a group also has certain drawbacks. It increases competition within the group for benefits such as access to food, acquiring a sexual partner or for occupying a safe and comfortable resting place.

Relationships within animal groups vary according to the type of association established. In open groups, as in insect swarms, bird flocks or fish schools, which are associations an individual can join or leave at any time, social contacts are loose and infrequent. Members of such a group are more or less equal. Formation of individual social contacts occurs only when the group members lose their anonymity, such as when the neighbouring birds of a nest colony can identify each other.

A different situation exists in a closed group. Even members of this group may still be anonymous, but they have a common language with which they can make their association known and disclose strangers who do not know the password. The 'language' is very often their common smell. This may either be produced by their scent glands or be acquired by the group from outside sources. Some members of rodent, peccary and marsupial glider groups produce a uniform scent within their set, rubbing each other with their urine or secretions from their dermal glands. In contrast, the bees' special colony odour is blended from the fragrances of whatever flowers they visited most often that particular season. Experiments performed on bumblebees have shown that the colony's identification mark is indeed the scent, and not any differences that show up in the behaviour of strangers. Worker bumblebees stung to death the strange bees placed in their nest but never attacked their own nestmates. However, when some of their nestmates were caged and put into a strange colony for two hours in order to absorb the foreign scent and then released back into their home colony, their sisters attacked them as if they were intruders.

In the most advanced social organizations, as found in many vertebrates, the individual members of the group know one another. Everybody is aware of his or her position in the class structure, one's own social rank. Such an arrangement, quite familiar to us all, is called social hierarchy. The surprising thing about this is that the scientists only began to recognize this fact about animals in the 1920s. The discovery is connected with the name of Danish naturalist T. Schjelderub-Ebbe. As a boy, he spent long hours watching the behaviour of chickens on his parents' farm. He noticed that individual hens in the flock were not equal, that a higher-ranking hen could peck at any lower class individual. The one who ruled could peck all the others and nobody dared retaliate. Schjelderub-Ebbe called the phenomenon 'the pecking order', and the term has been used by ethologists to designate the ranking order of other animals as well.

The top ranking animal is called Alpha, the next one in the order is Beta, then Gamma, and so on to the creature at the bottom of the social hierarchy, who is called Omega. Although Omega is the weakest, most overlooked and vulnerable one, that does not mean that the others can take out their aggression on it. While it is true that Omega is allowed to feed only when the other chickens have had their fill, still it enjoys special favours and protection from the leader of the flock; if Beta or Gamma attacks it for no apparent reason, Alpha will punish them. The ruling chicken is sensitive to the aggressive acts of the subordinates and its authority suppresses such attacks within the group. This guarantees law and order within the

A male Diana monkey (*Cercopithecus diana*) exposes the conspicuous hairs on his inner thighs when trying to impose and intimidate another male.

society. For group leaders, every privilege carries with it a responsibility. Alpha is the first to feed, gets the finest available food, sleeps in the most comfortable and safest place, and, if it is a male, he usually fathers most of the offspring. In return for these benefits, the leader bears the duty of keeping the group safe. When encountering an enemy, Alpha is the one most endangered, being expected to lead the defence. The authority of the chief is based on its experience as well as its physical abilities. This was documented by field observations made on Japanese macaques (*Macaca fuscata*). The group of monkeys was led by an old experienced male. One day the old leader was thrown over by a young male. The retired leader was made to live a life of seclusion. Then Japanese zoologists set loose a savage dog on the macaques, that attacked the monkeys and bit several of them. The strong but

The beautiful lion-tailed macaque (*Macaca silenus*) can also get very angry.

young leader, who had never before encountered this kind of enemy, hastily took to the treetops with the rest of the group. This was just the chance the old leader needed. He adroitly side-stepped when the dog charged him, grabbed the cur's tail and flung him over the cliff, into the sea. The fickle monkeys at once joined their old captain and assisted him in driving the young leader away.

Maintaining one's position in the social hierarchy would be a costly and demanding activity if each animal had constantly to fight for its place. Luckily, a rich repertoire of displays and expressions has evolved, which serves to demonstrate strength and to intimidate opponents before a real fight gets started. Among these ways of making others stand back are various facial expressions, gestures, imposing postures and vocal threats. On the other hand, low-ranking individuals, when trying to prevent an attack by a stronger individual, express their loyalty and subordination by submissive gestures. These means of communication, which are used for social contacts, do not significantly differ from those observed in use during territorial conflicts or for defence.

When striking a threatening pose, animals make use of any weapons at their disposal. Stallions curl back their lips to show powerful teeth. A similar threat yawn is performed by beasts of prey or baboons to warn intruders to stay away. This signal has even been carried over into human non-verbal symbolism. Does not the yawning grimace of the theatrical mask give the same message? A threatening bird aims its beak at the opponent. Another tactic for the intimidation of an adversary is optically to increase one's silhouette by bristling the hair or feathers. During times of strong emotion, humans can also feel contractions of the subtle dermal muscles which can make our short hair stand on end. Our goose pimples, however, would hardly scare anybody away. Some animals, when threatening, turn sideways to the enemy as the cat does, enhancing the enlarged contours of their arched bodies. Even an enraged elephant 'rattles his sabres' before attacking: it lifts its head and stretches out its earflaps. The visual impression is augmented by pawing the ground with its forelegs, swaying from side to side, whipping its tail and trumpeting loudly.

A threatening male ape shakes the tree branches vigorously or, in captivity, rattles the cage bars. A gorilla will snap off branches and beat the ground with them or pound its chest with its fists. A chimpanzee will threaten by bristling the hairs on

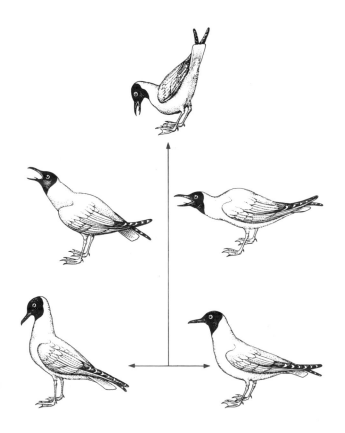

Five displays of the black-headed gull (*Larus ridibundus*) which occur in interactions of these birds. Each of them expresses a different degree of aggressiveness. The postures on the left mean readiness for attack, those on the right a tendency for retreat, motivation of the birds increasing from bottom to top. The posture shown in the middle, called choking, represents a state of the bird in which the tendencies for attack and retreat are balanced but the bird is still highly motivated.

145

its body and demonstrate its strength by rhythmically drumming on hollow tree trunks. An English zoologist, Dr. Jane Lawick-Goodall, described an interesting case of social climbing. Mike, a young wild chimpanzee, happened upon an empty barrel and used it as a drum. The mighty noise, much louder than the sound produced by pummelling on tree trunks, gained him respect and esteem among other members of the group. The African guereza monkeys merely smack their lips when trying to coerce an opponent, and the Diana monkey (*Cercopithecus diana*) exposes the conspicuous orange hairs on its inner thighs. The vervet monkey (*C. aethiops*) threatens by displaying his brightly coloured genitals and the proboscis monkey (*Nasalis larvatus*) intimidates his rivals with an erected penis. The enraged mangabey (*Cercocebus* sp.) shows his stark white eyelids — a rather comical gesture to a human — but a strong and unambiguous message for another monkey.

The mood of an animal can be detected by the position of its ears or tail. The flattened-back ears of large cats signify an imminent attack and zoo attendants or circus tamers know to respect and promptly respond to the cue. The porcupines (*Hystrix*) make menacing and vigorous movements of the tail, giving off a strange rattling noise made by its short hollow spines. The rattlesnake has a rattle at the end of its tail, composed of segments, which when it is excited, it shakes like a set of maracas.

In contrast to threat gestures are the expressions of submissiveness which are often derived from the behaviour of the young. A subordinate individual tries to win the sympathy of a stronger one by mimicking, usually only symbolically, the behaviour of the young. A defeated dog, for instance, exposes its belly, licks the mouth of a dominant animal or sometimes even wets itself. All these actions awake maternal behaviour in the winner, who begins to clean the underdog with its tongue. A defeated wolf offers its throat to the victor for biting. Dangerous weapons are, as a rule, pronouncedly turned away from the opponent. The crow, gull or crane swivels its head around, withdrawing its beak and exposing the vulnerable nape of its neck for pecking. Some animals, such as the squid, cichlid fish or certain species of lizards, change their colour as a sign of submissiveness. In animals that live in groups, submissive gestures have a form of ritualized greeting.

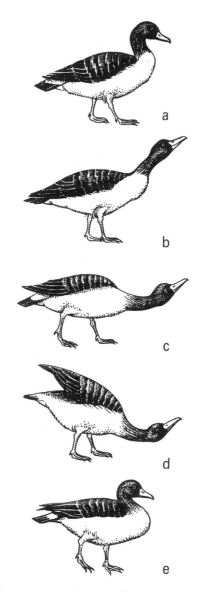

A goose as well as a wolf can express their moods unambiguously by different body postures: a — the quiet posture, b — the

Some lizards try to intimidate each other and to show their social position simply by changing their colour. This ability can be found among chameleons, agamas and, as documented by these pictures, also in anolises. A normally green specimen of *Anolis porcatus* (left) turns brown when frightened (right).

146

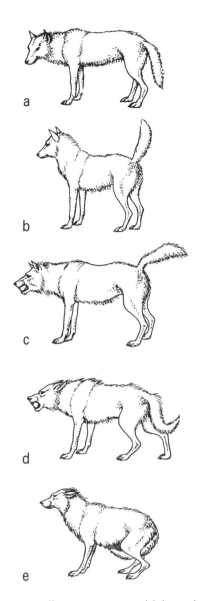

On his return home, a dog's master may be welcomed in a dog-like way: the dog jumps at him in an attempt to lick his mouth. Puppies learn appeasement gestures when playing with their father. He plays rather roughly with his young, forcing them to display the necessary appeasement rituals they will need to know in real fights later on.

A little understood aspect of animal communication is the one that deals with the pheromones which social species use to contribute toward establishing and maintaining the social hierarchy within the group. Many animals can recognize their fellow group member's social status by smell alone. The scent markings of dominant individuals are most distinctive from those of submissive ones. High-ranking animals have larger scent glands, containing more pheromone, which allows them to mark more frequently. This has been observed largely in guinea pigs, rabbits and mice. However, there may also be a qualitative difference in the chemical message of the dominant individual. The leader of a mouse clan has a smell which is powerfully attractive to all receptive females but causes subordinate males to give him a wide berth.

Compounds that can rightly be called fear pheromones or alarm odours have been discovered in several animals. When a black-tailed deer (*Odocoileus hemionus columbianus*) is chased, it excretes a special odour from the metatarsal glands on the inner side of the hind legs. Other deer will go out of their way to avoid any objects marked with this fear-inducing odour. Some deer in great stress will even augment the effects of the secretions by urinating on their own legs. An alarmed woodchuck (*Marmota monax*) everts its anal glands, giving off a secretion which has the effect of causing other woodchucks to lay low for a while. Brown rats (*Rattus norvegicus*) have also been observed to mark danger by defecating or urinating on poisonous bait. Allegedly, other members of the group then avoid the peril.

In the last couple of decades, ethologists have been increasingly discontent with observations made on animals in captivity. Some of them armed themselves with notebook, binoculars and camera as well as a considerable amount of patience and set out to spend long weeks or months in the company of apes in the jungle, lions in

threat to a distant opponent with imposing, c — the threat before attack, d — the threat mixed with fear, e — the submissive posture.

147

the savanna, seals on remote ocean beaches, chamois in alpine mountains and deer or wild pigs in forest preserves. If they succeeded in insinuating themselves into the company of these social animals, gaining their confidence, or at least their tolerance, the field studies brought significant and unexpected results.

Not surprisingly, most of their attention was devoted to field studies of apes. Of all animals, social communication in these primates is the most developed, sharing many of the communicative expressions which man has. A significant tool for communication is facial pantomime. All primates have a hairless face with well-developed facial muscles. Consequently, an ape can express with its face all possible feelings and intentions in astounding details.

In addition to facial expressions, primates make use of numerous gestures and symbolic movements. There is little actual fighting among the group, since threat gestures of the dominant animal usually suffice to pacify lower-ranking animals. However, social order is not based only on threat and intimidation. Many expressions are intended to assure, maintain and strengthen good relationships among group members. Chimpanzees, for instance, can express their friendly and peaceful intentions, or their joy at meeting, with a kiss. It is nothing but a ritualized behaviour derived from feeding the young mouth-to-mouth. Another greeting gesture, offering the hand, also comes from the mother-child relationship. A submissive individual stretches out its hand in the same way as do the young when soliciting food or toys. The dominant individual lightly touches the offered hand with the fingers to show its friendly attitude. If the dominant animal offers its hand first, the submissive individual is supposed to kiss it. Should the leader of the group wish to express its benevolence and amicable motives most explicitly, it lays its hand on the subordinate's head or neck. It is not difficult for us to interpret these greetings, since we use them ourselves in a similar context. The greeting of the baboons, however, will seem to us somehow awkward, if not rude. A young male stands with his back to the superior, bends, and exposes his colourful buttocks. As an expression of greatest deference he lifts his tail. The greeting apparently has its origin in mating behaviour, for the female invites the male for copulation with the same gesture. The response of the superior confirms this idea: in most cases, he mounts the young fellow to express his superiority.

Grooming, often mistakenly supposed to be for getting rid of fleas, actually serves to maintain and strengthen social bonds. These mutual touches act as appeasement signals and expressions of closeness, not to mention their hygienic importance.

Much has already been said about the vocal communication of monkeys in connection with their territorial behaviour (see the first section). The apes (Pongidae), too, use some acoustic signals, especially when danger approaches, but usually only to draw attention to themselves and to emphasize other warning behaviour. The morphology of their larynx and the limited mobility of their tongues prevent them from forming articulated vocal signals to the same extent that humans can do. That is why all attempts to teach chimpanzees or gorillas to talk have failed. Recently, researchers achieved more significant success by finding a common language with these large apes. They had to use a different approach. By taking advantage of the inherent abilities of the primates to gesticulate, they attempted to teach the apes American Sign Language (Ameslan), the language of the deaf. The results were astonishing. In 22 months, the young female chimpanzee Washoe learned 34 signs, eight times more words than another chimpanzee, Viki, succeeded in learning to pronounce during six long years of intensive study. In the next two years, Washoe mastered 132 signs, and she used them in situations similar to those in which children first use words when they are learning to speak.

The success with the chimpanzee inspired a young student of Stanford University in California, Francine 'Penny' Peterson, to conduct a daring experiment. She decided to teach a young gorilla female, Koko, Ameslan. Her attempt was a big success. Penny proved that gorillas are at least as intelligent as chimpanzees, then

150

Expressions of the hairless primate's face are readily understandable even to men. From the ape's face one can almost read the animal's thoughts.

considered the smartest of all apes. After six years of instruction, during which Penny and Koko lived together under one roof, the working vocabulary of Koko contained around 375 signs, including airplane, navel, lollipop, friend and stethoscope. Koko could answer as well as ask questions; she could tell her companion when she felt happy and when sad, refer to the past or future events, and she could formulate definitions of subjects. She also showed an impish sense of humour, she could insult her companion and occasionally she told a lie to avoid punishment.

Let us leave the university campus for a while and return, with the apes and monkeys, to the jungles and savannas. The rise in social position is determined by different qualities in females than it is in males. The rank of a female is strongly dependent on her physiological conditions. She ranks highest if she is ready to be fertilized. In baboons, gorillas or chimpanzees, this readiness is obvious from the first glance at her swollen pink buttocks. In other monkeys, the males taste the female's urine in order to ascertain her reproductive condition. A female with a baby also ranks high and enjoys special privileges. In addition, a female can make her way into better society by attracting a high-ranking male.

Even male monkeys have means other than threats or fight to gain a higher social rank. A sure method is making friends with a male of upper social status. Another smart manoeuvre is to play the role of favourite uncle to the youngsters of one's superiors. It has also been a common occurrence in baboons for three males who

were subordinate to the leader to form a triumvirate. When they act jointly, not even the strongest leader will dare to oppose them. Over a period of time, the self-appointed triad can take over the leadership of the group.

The strongest male usually fathers most of the offspring, but that does not mean he copulates the most frequently. Observations on one baboon group showed that the superior males preferred females that were in the fertile days of their reproductive cycles. The lesser males mated indiscriminately with females in all phases of the cycle. Thus they copulated often but with little chance of becoming fathers.

The Indian jungle is the home of a beautiful monkey that is considered sacred by the natives. The family life of the hanuman langur (*Presbytis entellus*) is far from being a saintly one. The first reports were made by Dr. Sarah B. Hrdy, who spent, together with her husband, over 1500 hours observing the langurs on Abu Mountain in Southwest Rajasthan. Female monkeys live in a group led by a single male. The rest of the males form a 'men's club', in which they seemingly rue their eunoch-like existence having lost any prospects for family life and the joys it brings. Now and again they make a raid on some of the orderly harems, driving away the original master and seizing all the females. Then a bloody fight commences among the males in which the strongest chases off the bachelor horde. The new master immediately takes steps to begin his own family. His first business is to kill all the offspring from the previous leader. He then fertilizes all the mothers, who go into oestrus as a result of their interrupted lactation. His murderous behaviour has a biological purpose. It assures that only his own young and no others profit from his role as leader and protector. In addition, it speeds up the reproduction of his own genes.

Mutual care of hair in horses and zebras is a social obligation among members of the herd.

152

The most social mammals do not live in the tropical jungle but rather on the desolate stony beaches of small Pacific islands. These are sea lions and walruses. Traditionally they gather on these remote, inhospitable places in hundreds of thousands to reproduce. The spot is chosen for the safety it offers during the delicate and vulnerable times of giving birth to their cubs and the love-making fests that follow soon after. Next year another generation will be born on exactly the same beach. The male fur seals (*Callorhinus ursinus*) will appear a bit sooner than the females at their traditional locations on two tiny Pribilov Islands in the Bering Sea. There they engage in fierce and often bloody fights for a small stretch of sandy beach, which will become their sovereign territory for the coming season and where no male trespassers will be tolerated. The largest and strongest males occupy the prime sections of the beach with the finest sand. The weaker members of the colony must make do with territory further from the sea or, worse, too close to the sea, under the hightide mark, where for a certain time only the head of the animal can be seen above the water.

A couple of weeks later, the first female seals arrive. They scramble up from the water, which has been their home for most of the year, and clumsily flop along on their bellies and flippers to those spots on the beach which they consider most suitable for giving birth to their young. Each male can only hope that it will be his territory which is chosen. A successful bull can acquire as many as 50 cows for his harem. A male without territory has no chance of winning the favour of even a single cow. Only a week after parturition the fur seals mate again. The female nevertheless will continue to suckle her newborn pup with her fat milk for many weeks without taking any food for herself.

The bulls of the elephant seal (*Mirounga angustirostris*) have a different strategy along the island beaches of the Mexican coast. They do not divide the beach into individual territories as do the fur seals. Instead, they compete for dominant status in such a way that the females can view the results and pick a hero. A male's rank is measured by the number of cows who choose to join his harem. A successful male may keep a large seraglio for several consecutive years and fertilize as many as 200 cows during that time. The struggle for social status does not happen without some fighting, and an encounter between a couple of two-metric tonne giants is a magnificent and dramatic spectacle. The battles are most violent at the beginning of the breeding season when the social relationships are being established. Later the ranks are maintained and occasionally tested by less violent means.

A harem of a Galapagos sea lion (*Zalophus californianus wollebaeki*) bull under the tropical sun of the Galapagos Archipelago.

A confrontation usually starts with stylized displays in which each of the bulls rears up on his front flippers and, with his proboscis extended into his mouth, he begins to blow threat calls. This by itself may suffice for each opponent to assess his chance of victory. The weaker one usually withdraws without fighting.

On Año Nuevo Island, zoologists have observed over 9000 such threat displays, of which only 60 ended up in real fights.

The bull's calling differs slightly in each individual, making it possible for the animals to recognize each other by voice. According to certain vocal characteristics, a male can reliably estimate the strength of his opponent without even seeing him. Hence the threatening roar can be heard even at night. The voice of the strongest bull sounds like the slow regular striking of the ultimate in large drums. A youngster's voice is much higher and has less regular sound pulses. American zoologists compared sonograms of male northern elephant seal calls from four different islands along the Pacific coast of California and Mexico. They found the most surprising array of acoustic differences. These seals seem to have their own dialects, similar to those found in bird songs.

A classic textbook example of an animal fight for rank and order is the jousting of the deer. It is one of the best understood social behaviours of large mammals, thanks to man's long-lasting interest in these spectacular game animals. For most of the year, however, deer are rather peaceful and tolerant animals living in small stable herds, the members of which know each other well. With the exception of the breeding season, social relations are established and maintained mainly by ritualized displays, postures and gestures. By means of this animal 'pantomime', every individual assesses the ability and strength of the others and constantly verifies his own position within the group.

Before the real fight breaks out, the buck deer exhibit the so-called parallel walk, during which they are trying to assess each other.

An unmistakable sign of dominance is expressed in the so-called direct sight (above left). It holds a strong charge of aggression and, as a rule, only a bold individual uses it against a considerably weaker one. It is not by chance that we rarely see these animals look each other straight in the eye. Neither individual can stand direct sight very long. A submissive animal will quickly run away (above right). Only an equal partner returns the threat or directly attacks. Of course,

The main means of communication in deer rituals are the position of the head, direction of sight and the degree of openness of the eyes. The position of the ears, the posture of the whole body and the way the tail is held are also of great significance.

The physical combat between two buck deer is a ritualized style of fighting in which each contestant tries to push the other backwards, or to the ground.

outside the breeding season the fight resembles rather a playful brawl which never results in serious injury to either contestant. The deer just bite (above left) or kick each other; sometimes the clash may culminate in the rearing up of both rivals and threatening or boxing with the forelegs. This is, however, a showy gesture rather than a real fight. If the bucks have already grown their antlers, a dominant individual threatens by stooping his head and pointing the antlers against the opponent, sometimes even pretending an attack (above right).

With the onset of the mating season the relationships among deer change dramatically. The groups fall apart and the males go away, often to distant mating places. Night after night a loud roar can be heard from there. The fights between the bucks now become violent and forceful, and the numbers of injured or fatally wounded individuals are far from negligible. For example, on the island of Rhum, Scotland, about one third of male red deer are wounded each year, and half of those die as a result of battle injuries. Still more dramatic statistics have been reported in continental Europe. In a fenced enclosure in Czechoslovakia, five of seven bucks found dead were stabbed by antlers and died of the wounds inflicted. No wonder that bucks try, if there is a choice, to avoid a direct confrontation even during the mating season. Certainly, they never take up an obviously lost cause.

The main means of assessing the strength of an adversary is the buck's roaring. Dr. Timothy Clutton-Brock of Cambridge University with his students has demonstrated this in a series of field experiments, in which he attempted to provoke bucks in rut to start a dialogue with a tape recorder. As he succeeded easily, it was clear that the males respond to and answer each other. Those who own a harem of does call more often than those without females. The buck calls most intensely when he is likely to be attacked. The frequency of exchange of vocal threats increases as the rival approaches. The roaring buck always stands on that side of the harem from which the opponent responds, even if the intruder is represented merely by the voice of a hidden loudspeaker. By means of the playback technique, the Cambridge scientists made many interesting findings, showing, for instance, how important the frequency of vocal threats are in the enraged deer. Even when trying to intimidate each other at a long distance, the antlered rivals maintain certain protocol. Thus 'butting in' is against all social rules. The bucks usually take turns in roaring, and each one waits for about ten seconds for the answer. Should the scientist's tape recorder break the rule by responding sooner, the buck ignores its voice. At such a fast pace the animal simply has no time to respond. The frequency of calls may also be used for predicting the course and outcome of the approaching encounter. The zoologists claim to have been able to predict the winner with great accuracy. He usually called more often during the last five minutes before the clash. The pattern of calling frequency even seemed to suggest whether or not the fight would occur. If the challenger managed to call more often than the defender, a fight usually ensued; if not, the challenger most likely pulled out.

The voice characteristics not only reveal the distance and direction of the challenger's approach, they also tell a lot about the opponent's fighting abilities. The leading bucks, owners of large harems of does, did not show any interest when the ethologists challenged them with a playback of the voice of young, i.e. less powerful, males. They did, however, respond to a playback of equal partners.

The harem owners do not roar only when threatened. They call more or less all day long, letting everybody know that the harem has its master. Such tooting of one's own horn may not always pay off. If a young male of five or six years of age succeeds in getting his own small herd of does, he does not call much. Even bachelor bucks surpass him in calling. If nothing is at stake the stripling brazenly struts to display his strength, because, if his bluff is called, he can easily take off. If he has does, however, this would not be so easy; that is why the youngsters are better off not calling at all. They must not lose face before the females, however, and therefore they vocalize occasionally.

Roaring is not the only way deer assess strength. When the two rivals draw near, they do not attack each other at once. After their exchange of vocal threats, the game of nerves continues. Most of the real fights are preceded by the so-called parallel walk, which may last for a few seconds or several minutes (see the picture at the bottom of p. 154). The long walks are usually made by rivals who are closely matched after the vocal disputes. The longer the time they need for assessing each other, the more likely it is that one of them will not be able to stand the tension and will abandon the scene without a fight. Parallel walking bucks make a strange picture; both fix their eyes straight ahead, because the slightest movement of the head toward the rival is an unambiguous invitation to fight. The opponent responds to such a challenge with lightning speed and both bucks find themselves locked by their antlers.

The honey bee queen (marked with a white dot) solicits the attentiveness and care of the worker bees by means of the queen substance, a social pheromone which the members of her colony eagerly lick from the surface of her body.

THE ROYAL PERFUME

Division of duties in a bee colony

Bee, ant or termite societies may contain tens of thousands of individuals, yet the reproduction of the colony is dependent on a very few members of the group, and even, as in bees or termites, on a single queen. She maintains her exclusive position among her nestmates by powerful chemical means in the form of pheromones. A closer study of the everyday life of a honey bee society reveals a fascinating story.

The majestic presence of the queen bee is the strongest tie to the home nest for every member of this six-legged society. The strength of her personality is most dramatically apparent immediately around her. When watching the crowds surrounding her, one almost feels that it must be some kind of honour or privilege to be near the queen, to touch her, eventually to lick or even feed her. The queen's magic is imparted through a pheromone called, logically enough, the queen substance, which is produced in her mandibular glands. The main component of the queen substance was isolated and identified as E-9-oxo-2-decenoic acid. The importance of this compound for the regulation of all activities in the colony can be vividly demonstrated by removing the queen from a prosperous colony. In less than half an hour life within the hive changes. The colony becomes restless and agitated. Worker bees become disoriented and occasionally attack each other. Within the next few hours they rebuild one or more comb cells into emergency queen cells.

Early in summer, at the beginning of the swarming season, daily production of the queen substance falls below the minimum demand of 0.1 micrograms per bee. The worker bees, bereft of normal inhibitions, begin building several queen cells at the edge of the comb. The queen deposits one egg in each cell. The larvae that hatch from the eggs are fed a highly nutritious food, the royal jelly, so that in an unbelievably short time, a mere 16 days, new queens leave the royal cells.

Male bees and other male hymenopterans have only half the usual number of chromosomes (haploid number), because they arise from unfertilized eggs. Worker bees are genetically females with undeveloped sex organs and possessing a complete (diploid) set of chromosomes.

The larvae in these cells will be given royal treatment, being fed a special diet of royal jelly in order to make them develop into a new queen — the saviour of the colony. During the temporary absence of the queen, the ovaries of some worker bees will develop and the bees will lay unfertilized eggs, from which only drones will result.

The stir in an orphaned bee colony can be quieted to a certain extent by inserting a wick soaked with synthetic oxodecenoic acid into the hive, thus demonstrating that the queen substance is a pheromone which prevents the worker bees from ripening their own eggs and building new queen cells. In addition to this, it has manifold other effects on the bodily functions and behaviour of the worker bees. One of the functions is helping to maintain order and discipline among members of the bee society. When the queen is present, it takes only 50 worker bees to construct a comb. Without her royal presence, it takes ten thousand bees to accomplish the same task.

In order to maintain her powerful influence over the colony, the queen must dole out about 0.1 microgram of her substance to each member. In a hive of 80 thousand members, that means she must produce a total of approximately eight milligrams of the acid daily. During her four-year life-span the production may amount to one millilitre. In our terms that would be a thimbleful of this precious essence;

compared to her size, however, it equates to about a bathtubful! Of course, not all her subjects can make daily contact with the queen. They must rely on emissaries to spread the chemical to them. Worker bees are eager for the substance, as if it were a daily fix for their addiction. This explains their restlessness when they suddenly lose their queen. The bees are able to break down the substance quickly into inactive metabolites. It is believed that the worker bees feed these broken-down products back to the queen, for it is she alone who can convert them into the much-needed and desired pheromone.

Before describing the other functions of the queen substance, let us briefly recapitulate how the honey bee colony reproduces. Its life cycle begins with swarming. We do not know all the factors that cause the bees to swarm, although overcrowding is undoubtedly one of them.

While the colony is nursing new queens in the queen cells, the behaviour of the old queen changes as dramatically as that of her workers. Everybody gets ready for swarming. The old queen deposits her last eggs and her abdomen shrinks to a slim profile. She becomes fidgety and irritated. The worker bees decrease her food rations and their former esteem for her wanes. They crawl over her and kick her until she is forced to leave the hive. The svelte royalty, with an entourage of worker bees, flies a short distance away and lands on a branch or other solid object. Her followers form a dense cluster around her. A flying queen still attracts the worker bees with her queen substance; however, the chemical composition is altered slightly after she lands and a related hydroxydecenoic acid prevails. Only the bees closest to her can smell it, but they in turn emit their own attractant from the Nassanoff glands on the back of their abdomen, which calls the others.

In the meantime, the scout bees set off on exploratory flights in all directions to search for a suitable site for their new home. If a scout finds such a place, she returns to communicate its location to the swarm with a dance similar to the one foragers use in the hive to indicate a new source of food (see the next chapter). The more suitable the site, the more vigorously the bee dances. Quite often it happens that more than one scout proclaims a new site and an interesting competition commences. Other bees, recruited by one or other of the scouts' dancing, fly off to check the claims for themselves. The one they like best is then touted by them also. Thus the most attractive and suitable places are gradually promoted by more and more dancers, while the scout bees publicizing inferior sites are excluded from 'the game'. The competition is over when all the dancing bees agree on one site. The swarm then collectively moves to the selected place. Dr. Martin Lindauer, who discovered the remarkable communication behaviour in swarming bees, made immediate, successful predictions on the location of the future nest site by observing the bees' dance. He could then get to the place ahead of the swarm. The German professor could therefore be said to be the first man to be sent by bees to a designated place.

Coming back to look at the old original hive, we can see that about one third of the worker bees stayed behind to await the emergence of the new queen. Concurrent with the creation of the queen cells, or even sooner, groups of larger cells appeared on the comb, into which the old queen had laid unfertilized eggs. These would give rise to drones. After hatching, they spend about four days of lazy life in the hive before they become sexually mature. Then they set off for their nuptial flight to meet the new queens from other colonies.

The queen that emerges first from the queen cell is without competition at the beginning. Her mother has already left with the swarm and her sisters have not yet emerged. She walks through the hive and searches for her sibling rivals, exchanging peeping sounds with them that the human ear can easily detect. The newly emerged

The queen substance is a powerful attractant to the swarming bees. The worker bees will cluster around their queen in whatever place she chooses to rest, be it a movie camera.

The unity of the honey bee swarm is maintained by the queen through the queen substance, until the scout bees find a suitable shelter for a new colony nest.

queens challenge each other, the strongest one driving her rivals out of the nest or stinging them to death, often while they are still in their queen cells. The impatient worker bees soon force the new reigning queen to leave the hive for her first nuptial flight. In the future her queen substance will be used for its number one role — to control the colony. On this first exit, however, it is issued for another purpose — to call in the grooms.

If the weather is fine, all the drones leave their respective hives in various locations to gather in throngs in a certain place high in the air where they unerringly, in annual tradition, await the queens. As soon as a queen crosses the imaginary boundaries of the trysting place, the attention of the male swarm is all on her. The drone who succeeds in being the first to land on her back in mid-air will find the queen's open sting chamber with the tip of his abdomen. His genitals literally explode into her womb. These are the last seconds of the drone's life. His dying body falls back, leaving some five million spermatozoids in the queen's spermatheca. In the following days, the queen repeats her nuptial flights and mate with other drones. The sperm she collects in her stormy youth will have to last the rest of her several years of life. If she exhausts them too soon, she will lay only unfertilized eggs, from which only drones will develop.

The reason for these long and perilous excursions is, apparently, to prevent inbreeding. Drones fly much longer distances than queens do, making it unlikely that they would mate with a queen from their own nest. The worker bees within one colony are not all true sisters either, although they have a common mother. Since the queen does a lot of mating during her nuptial flights, her offspring may have six to ten different fathers.

LOOKING FOR FOOD

Living in societies has another practical advantage. By working together, the animals can obtain food more easily. If there is not enough food of an appropriate size available, predatory animals may co-operatively subdue and kill an animal much larger than any of them could handle individually. Thanks to such collaborative hunting techniques, the species can occupy an ecological niche otherwise reserved for much larger and stronger predators. However, even smaller but numerous prey can sometimes be more easily rounded up and dealt with by a group. If one member of a society discovers an ample source of food, it may invite the others to the feast. The bounty can thus be more easily defended against encroachers. Finally, there are cases in which one animal can profit from a negative experience of another, for instance by finding a message that a place under consideration has already been searched and found lacking in food.

All these and other possible advantages of the communal method of obtaining food assume a certain degree of organization in feeding behaviour. The co-ordination of various activities of team hunters or foragers has the prerequisite of a common language. Some of the components of its vocabulary will be examined in the following chapters.

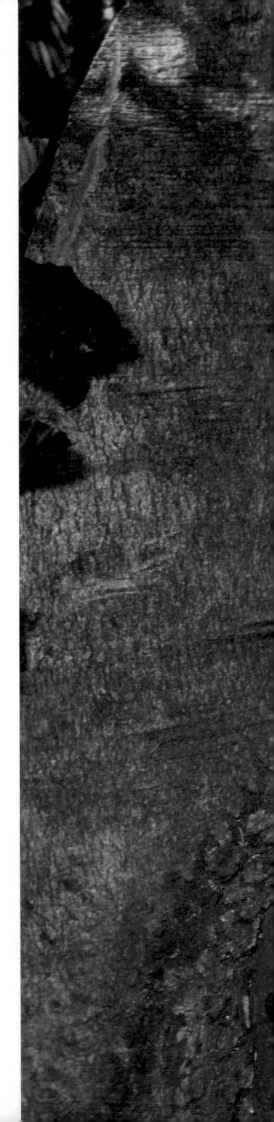

When two ants meet, they do not shake hands, but they 'shake antennae'. By doing this, they introduce and identify themselves with their scent. Instead of talking about weather, they talk about the current status of their stomachs. If it happens that one of them has a crop which is fuller than the other, it willingly shares its contents with its comrade.

Mutual feeding is an everyday duty, not only among ants but in all social insects. The phenomenon is called trophallaxis, which means the exchange of liquid food. Worker ants have greatly expandible crops, which may even extend down into the abdomen. These foragers can haul amazingly large loads of food from the feeding area back to the nest. There they distribute the food among the younger ants, who were fulfilling their household duties. The full ant feeds the hungry ones until they are equally full. This altruistic need to feed everybody who is hungry leads to establishing a kind of 'social stomach'. Everyone learns from the state of its own crop the state of the whole society.

A hungry ant, bee or wasp asks to be fed by its full nestmate with a complex antennal language. The begging is obviously eloquent, for if an ant parasite learns it, it secures his place on the dole. Food brought into the nest is quickly distributed throughout the society. This was demostrated by an experiment performed on bees. Six foragers were allowed to feed on 20 millilitres of sugar water marked with radioactive phosphorus. Five hours later, the radioactive marker was found in 28 per cent of the hive's population and, 24 hours later, in 55 per cent of their nestmates. This is astounding considering that a bee colony has several tens of thousands of members.

The apportionment of food may not always be so equitable. For instance, the queens or males in ant societies are certainly getting more food than they personally contribute. In worker ants of *Formica polyxena*, those with undeveloped ovaries are preferentially fed with honeydew, whereas workers producing the so-called trophic eggs are fed predominantly on proteins from the blood of prey. The explanation of this behaviour is simple. The group of ants fed with honeydew is composed of old, experienced foragers. They need energy for long food-gathering excursions. Those ants which are egg-layers are younger nurse ants. They require proteins for feeding the brood and the queen. It is still a mystery how ants can express their specific needs by their antennal language.

Less idyllic relationships exist among the yellow-jackets and hornets. Worker wasps are not all equal. There is a primitive social hierarchy in their nests which applies even to feeding. A dominant worker gets more than she gives. If a subordinate worker fails to respect her request for food, the dominant one issues a threat. The queen, of course, takes food without giving any in return. Male wasps, which are unable to provide food for themselves, are the most disadvantaged members of the colony. They rely solely on what they can snatch away from two mutually feeding workers, or what they can get by begging from the larvae. The larvae participate in the exchange of food with adults by releasing a droplet of salivary secretion which the adult wasp quickly imbibes. The saliva is both tempting and nutritious; so the salivary glands of larvae act as the pantry to the wasp colony in the same way as the social stomach operates in the ants. Recently it was discovered that larvae supply worker wasps with sugars which adults are unable to derive from proteins. Adults need these sugars to fuel their flight muscles, but only larvae possess all the enzymes necessary for breaking down the proteins.

Perhaps even more remarkable is the way in which the wasp brood asks for food. The larvae produce rhythmically coded sounds by rubbing their mandibles against the wall of their paper comb. This sound not only informs the nurse wasp how hungry the larva is but also indicates its age. An artificial sound simulator, placed by

FOLLOW YOUR NOSE

Trail pheromones

Workers of many ant species lay eggs with which they feed the queen and, less frequently, the other workers. These trophic eggs are usually small, irregular in shape and often lacking a shell. In the species Atta rubripilosa *they even fuse, so that the material which leaves the oviduct is a sort of extra nutritious omelette.*

The largest social wasp, the European hornet (*Vespa crabro*), feeding the brood.

In ants (left) and bees (right), mutual exchange of liquefied food is a standard duty among the members of the worker caste.

a researcher on the bottom of an empty comb cell, played back the sounds of a larva soliciting food. Nurse wasps were attracted to the cell and continued to pile food into it as long as the sound emanated from there.

The ways social insects inform themselves about new sources of food, and how they manage to send their nestmates to these places, are the most fascinating features of their social lives. Ants depend exclusively on scent signals for this purpose. If an ant worker meets a prey larger than she can handle herself, she simply releases an alarm pheromone, which arouses other workers in the immediate vicinity. They then jointly subdue the prey.

The next step in the ladder of complexity of chemical communication used to recruit helpers has been dubbed 'tandem running'. This behaviour has been observed in many species and described in great detail in a tiny ant, *Leptothorax acervorum*. When a scout ant finds an abundant supply of food, she will offer a free sample from the contents of her crop to whichever nestmates happen to be close by. She then turns her back to them, raising her abdomen high in the air. A tiny drop of liquid will appear on the tip of her protruding sting. This is a strong attractant for the other workers, and with it the successful explorer challenges them to follow her. When one of the onlookers touches her with the antennae, the scout ant heads in a straight line toward the food with her stinger still raised like a flag. She is followed by only one worker, who constantly touches her. If, for some reason, the follower slows down and loses contact, or if we deliberately hold her back, the leader will stop, raise her abdomen and repeat her scented challenge once again. If we then

If a worker ant meets a larger prey than she can handle herself, she simply releases an alarm pheromone, which arouses other workers in the immediate vicinity. They then jointly subdue the prey.

gently tickle her abdomen with a fine hair, she will resume her run. This demonstrates how important it is for the leader to feel the touch of the recruited nestmate, for whom in turn the smell of the leader is of sole importance. The nestmate will just as easily follow the head of a pin, if it is dipped in an extract from the sting gland.

In most ants, the evolution of their communication system did not stop at this stage. The leader no longer releases a cloud of volatile scent into the air. Instead she lowers her abdomen to spew the pheromone along the ground. This scented trail lasts longer and gives more nestmates a chance to follow it. At first, the scent was still quite volatile so that only a few ants could be guided by it. In more advanced species, the durability of the trail marks increased and the followers learned to restore the faded marks with their own scent. This led to the development of a fantastically efficient technique of chemical communication, namely trail pheromones.

The first evidence for the existence of these pheromones was produced by a Swiss entomologist, Charles Bonnet, as early as in 1779. Anybody can easily repeat his experiment: if a finger wet with saliva is rubbed across the route of an ant trail, a miniature highway on which multitudes of ants run in both directions, the result is pandemonium. Throngs of bewildered ants on either side of the imaginary barrier made by the saliva will build up in a matter of seconds. It may take a minute or so for the first bold ant to cross the great divide and to restore the flow of traffic on the road.

If we linger for a close watch on the ant trail, quite a few interesting details can be noticed. The ants never walk in a straight line. They always zig-zag as if bouncing off imaginary banks on either side of the road. That is because they are not detecting scent directly from the ground, but they are running in a scented 'tunnel' made of pheromone vapours above the trail. The boundaries of the tunnel are detected by their outstretched antennae. If we cut off one of these, the ant will keep to the side of the road on which she has the remaining sensory organ. From the other side, she receives no signal and apparently reads this lack of information as meaning that there is no trail on that side. The ant will be even more confused if her antennae are fixed in a crossed position by a droplet of glue. If she is able to follow the trail at all, she will more resemble a tavern customer leaving the bar after the last call than the diligent and industrious pilgrim. The same 'effect' can be reached if you try to ride a bicycle with your arms crossed.

Still another remarkable feature of the trail pheromones was discovered: they function as means of mass communication. The path leading to new resources is always marked by the scout who first discovered the place. Her trail is followed, to begin with, by a few worker ants who will reinforce the fading trail on their way back, provided they are carrying a substantial load of food. The stronger trail will entice more workers, who also contribute to the trail scent with their own pheromones. As a result of this, the crowds along the road increase exponentially. However, this will last only as long as the ants have something to collect. Frustrated latecomers return to the nest without reinforcing the trail. Thus the trail maintains an intensity of scent which is proportional to the amplitude of the supply, and the number of workers is regulated by the amount of labour required.

One can find troublesome pests even among otherwise likable ants. One of them, the pharaoh ant (*Monomorium pharaonis*), is a true blight to modern human dwellings in temperate regions all over the world, particularly in Europe. A prosperous life has been secured for these tiny ants within the confines of large blocks of flats because of their extraordinarily well-developed information system, based on trail pheromones. Omnipresent scout ants are ready in a flash to inform

The traffic jam on a highway leading from the nest of the American termites *Nasutitermes ripperti.*

The trail pheromones are mostly species specific. Only closely related species of ants can respond to each others' trails. The compound used for marking the trail is produced from various abdominal glands and in some ants also in the intestine.

their nestmates if a sandwich is left on the kitchen table, and within a few minutes the bread may be teaming with ants. One of the strategies considered for controlling pharaoh ants is to fight them with their own fire. A group of Dutch scientists has already identified the chemical structure of their trail pheromone. The compound was given the name faranal. The next step is to find out how to send these ants on the scented trail to their 'happy hunting grounds'.

Recently, trail pheromones were found also in the tent caterpillar moth of the

The fact that totally unrelated termites and ants have independently developed their own trail pheromones provides the best evidence for the usefulness of this communication system for terrestrial social insects. In advanced termites of the genus *Reticulitermes* and *Nasutitermes* (right), the trail pheromones are reportedly active in such extremely low concentrations that the trail laid down by them is supposed to be only a chain of single molecules.

genus *Malacosoma*. The caterpillars gather for the night or for moulting in dense silk nests. From there they spread all over the tree for daily grazing. Each larva, when leaving the nest, leaves behind a silk strand marked with a trail pheromone. In the evening, it will use the silk as a guiderope back to the nest, reinforcing the scent if it has been well fed. The next morning other nestmates follow those recruitment trails when looking for their own feeding grounds.

167

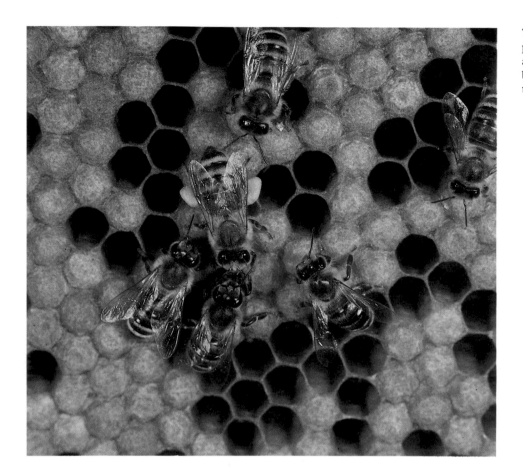

The forager honey bee (recognizable by the pollen baskets on her hind legs) offers a sample of the food to her nestmates before she begins to advertize location of the find by dancing.

The dances, which are the bees' way of communicating information about the location of distant sources of food, are considered to be the most advanced language of any invertebrates. In certain respects they have even been compared with the language of man. Whether or not such a comparison is justified, the honey bee dance language is nonetheless the most popular and has been the most thoroughly studied communication behaviour in animals. The deciphering of the bee dance code is inseparable from the name of Karl von Frisch. The Austrian professor proved that the most prominent element of the bee language, the waggle dance, is a complex signal describing the distance and direction of a food source. It is the method a dancer uses to send her nestmates to the place where she has just found food. In a rehearsal for the real flight they will soon make, the other bees follow and repeat the movements of the dancer. They must learn the route beforehand, as they are then sent out on their mission without a guide.

I invite you to take a closer look with me at what a bee says to her companions, and how she does so. There is hardly a more objective way to do this than to follow, step by step, the discoveries of the Nobel Prize winner, Professor von Frisch.

Young von Frisch began his first experiments shortly after World War I. He set out a dish filled with honey-sweetened water for the bees to find. The first forager to arrive at the syrup dish was marked by the scientist in order to distinguish her among thousands of other bees in a glass observation hive. Immediately on her return home, the marked bee offered a sample of the honey syrup to several of her nestmates and then began to dance. The type of dance she performed was given the name round dance. The dancing bee ran around excitedly, first describing a circle to the right, then to the left and then back to the right. Before leaving the hive to

HOW TO TEACH BEES TO TELL A LIE

Dance language of the honey bees

The round dance is used by the bees to indicate a source of food when it is near the hive.

Bees also may mark rich sources of pollen or nectar with an aggregation pheromone from their Nassonoff gland, which attracts other foragers.

collect another load, the marked forager repeated her dance in another location in the comb for a new group of spectators. With each dance performance, she excited the onlookers, who followed and repeated her movements, touching her with their antennae. Suddenly, one of them broke away from the cluster and left the hive, soon followed by the others. In rapid succession, they all appeared at the feeding place. When they returned home, they too danced. The more bees that danced, the more bees were seen at the feeding site. It was plain that the dance was an announcement of available food. It was unclear, however, how the bees recruited by the dance were able to find the feeding site.

In an attempt to find out whether the round dance contained any information about the direction in which the food source could be found, von Frisch offered food to several bees from a feeder ten metres west of the hive. He then placed three more feeders, all containing the syrup, equidistant from the hive at points east, north and south. A few minutes after the discoverers of the western site performed their dance, many new bees appeared simultaneously on all four feeders. The professor concluded that the round dance meant 'fly to look for food near the nest!'.

In Nature, obviously, the honey bees do not collect food from dishes but from flowers, and these have characteristic fragrances. In further experiments, von Frisch demonstrated that the bee has an acute sense of smell and an excellent memory for fragrances. This time he offered the sugar water to the bees on the fragrant blossoms of the cyclamen. When he put two vases of the flowers in the vicinity of the hive, one containing cyclamen, and the other phlox, the recruited bees were only interested in the blossoms of the cyclamen and totally ignored the phlox. This means that they were not looking for just any food, but for something in particular. The professor then repeated this experiment many times with blossoms of various fragrances and with scented syrups, and consistently got the same results. The bees apparently remember the scent with which the dancing forager is perfumed and set out to look for it. Thus von Frisch was the first to explain the biological function of the floral fragrances as a lure for pollinators. Some flowers, however, may be rich in nectar but may not have much of an odour. Yet the honey bees find and distinguish them by their sense of smell. That is because they mark the blossoms with their own attractant, which is secreted from the Nassanoff gland in the abdomen. The scented declaration left on the flower issues the call 'this is the place, come on everybody'.

For many of the years during which von Frisch performed his experiments with honey bees, he always placed the feeder in the immediate vicinity of the hive. This enabled him to watch the bees both at the feeder and in the hive. Occasional observations, however, caused him to wonder if the bees might even communicate information about the distance of new food sightings. After all, in Nature they do make collecting trips of several kilometres. The scientist decided to investigate his suspicion experimentally.

He set up two stations, one 10 metres and the other 300 metres from the hive. At first, when he offered food to marked foragers at the closer station, the recruited bees looked for the food, which was advertised by the dance, at this nearby location. When he then offered food at the distant station only, the newcomer bees appeared in numbers at that place exclusively. At the near station, so conveniently close to the hive, a negligible number showed up, although the recruited bees must have passed it on their way to the distant feeder. It became clear to the investigator that the forager bees must have provided information about the distance of the newly discovered source of food. By comparing the dance formations of bees advertising a close and a distant source, the professor found that the information is coded by the method of dancing. All foragers which were marked 10 metres from the hive performed a typical round dance, whereas foragers returning from the station 300 metres away danced in a completely different way; their dance had the form of a figure eight with a straightened central run. When the bee entered this straight run, she made a motion that could not but captivate even the attention of an uninformed human observer. The dancer rapidly wagged her tail, accompanying the action with rhythmic piping cries. Hence von Frisch named this type the tail-wagging dance, or simply the waggle dance. Slowly increasing the distance between the feeder and the hive, the scientist discovered that the bees gradually changed the round dance into the waggle dance when the food source was between 80 and 100 metres from the hive. When the professor with his students then moved the feeder still farther away, up to 10 kilometres, and simultaneously recorded changes in the dances of the returning foragers, he could conclude that the bees communicate the distance of the food source by the velocity of the dancing. When advertizing food 100 metres away, the bee made the figure-of-eight ten times in half a minute, at the distance of 300 metres only seven times, at 500 metres only six times, and so on. The bee forager returning from a 10 kilometres distant station made only one and a quarter figures in the 30 second interval. The semicircular parts of the figure were always run at the same speed, and the velocity of the dancing differed only in the straight run. While making this run the dancing bee emitted a peculiar buzz, as if pretending flight. A later acoustic analysis, performed by von Frisch's students, suggested that a substantial part of the dance information is coded only in those vibrations.

However accurate the indication of the distance of a new food supply, the bees would find the information useless unless complemented by directions which way to fly, reasoned Professor von Frisch. When observing more bees that all returned from the same feeder, he noticed that every one of them oriented their waggle dance in one direction. The straight runs were parallel in all cases. Also, the direction of the straight runs gradually changed during the day, the change corresponding roughly to the angle the sun had moved in the sky. The observer deduced that the forager bee has to remember the position of the sun relative to the direction of her flight path. When she returns to the darkness of the hive she communicates this angular deviation of her flight path from the direction of the sun by making the straight run at the same angle from the vertical. If, for instance, the bee runs straight upwards, she is saying, 'the food is in the direction of the sun'. If, on the other hand, she runs straight down, the advertised source is in the opposite direction from the sun. A straight run containing an angle of 20° to the right of the vertical says that the plant is 20° to the west of the radiant disc.

The conclusions made by the school of Professor von Frisch shook the scientific community, and not all biologists supported his theories. A particularly sharp criticism was raised by a Californian professor, Adrian M. Wenner. He and his students repeated von Frisch's experiments and came to the conclusion that the bees do not use the information communicated by the dance language for finding their way to a new food source. They did not deny the fact that the bees dance, nor that it is possible to read from the dance the location of the food. They refuted the idea that the bees actually read this information. The critics maintained that the bees are guided exclusively by their sense of smell.

Wenner's group developed a hypothesis of 'local scents', according to which the forager bees are well aware of various scents in the landscape around the colony nest, having a kind of scent map of the surroundings in their memory. The recruits pick up olfactory cues about the area where food was discovered (swamp, pine forest, heath etc.) and, using their excellent scent memory, they are able to find the

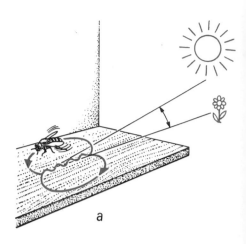

The waggle dance is used by the honey bees to communicate the distance and direction of the food source. The most important part of the dance figure is the straight run between the two circles. If the bee dances on the horizontal plate, the straight line points directly toward the source (a). In the darkness of the hive, it is diverged from the vertical axis by the same angle as the food source is diverged from the sun (b).

An excited honey bee worker calls her nestmates by means of an alarm pheromone released from the Nassanoff glands in her abdomen.

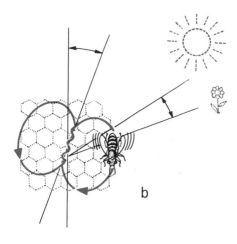

b

'Depending upon conditions, honey bee recruits use either the dance language and odour information, or odours alone... For example, when a single, abundant, and extensive crop is available, the odour of that source in the hive might grow strong enough to eliminate dance-language recruitment. However, even in the early stages, the dance language would be necessary to alert foragers to the new source... Alternatively, a single, abundant, extensive food source may be more typical of current agricultural practices than of the tropical forests in which the honey bee and its language evolved. In that case, the ability to direct recruits to a distant, isolated patch of food quickly — either before it was found by another colony or another species, or before the potentially brief period of blooming ended — might have been a real advantage. Only further work can establish whether the dance-language communication is common or rare under normal circumstances. Even a rare phenomenon may still be real, however and the dance language is a real and very significant phenomenon indeed.'

James L. Gould,
Science 189, 1973

source without further instructions. New experiments were carried out on both sides of the scientific battle line, but after several years of cross fire in the literature it would be fair to say that conclusive proof of either hypothesis was still lacking. A majority of the scientists favoured von Frisch but perhaps because they could not believe that the proven relationship between the form of the dance and the position of the food source would be without function. It seemed technically next to impossible to design an experiment that would bring a decisive verdict in favour of one of the hypotheses, if only because the olfaction hypothesis is difficult to totally disprove. It was necessary to have a bee perform a waggle dance indicating a particular place she had never visited. In other words, the bee would have to tell a lie to her nestmates. How could she be made to do so?

The ideal solution would seem to be a 'dummy' bee, designed to perform a dance under human control. The first attempt to fool the bees in this way was done by one of von Frisch's students some 40 years ago. Then, however, nothing was known about the significance of the sounds produced by the dancing bee. For this, and perhaps other reasons, the dummy failed. Several more sophisticated attempts have since been reported, involving dummies perfumed by the home scent of the colony and provided with mini-speakers, but nobody has ever persuaded bees to respond adequately to a model and follow its dances. At best, the bees merely tolerated the dancing puppet among themselves.

A student at Rockefeller University, James L. Gould, also tried his luck with a dummy bee and also failed, despite the fact that his model could sing and was provided with an artifical proboscis capable of releasing nectar to those requesting it. The ambitious student soon learned that if he was to successfully finish and defend his thesis, he had to attack the problem from a completely different angle.

Gould studied all the available literature on bee behaviour. He singled out a fact discovered several years ago, that if a small, bright, pin point source of light is provided at the side of the vertical comb, bees will often treat this as if it was the sun and angle their waggle run respective to the lamp. It seems that if this artificial light is strong enough, it overrides the influence of gravity, as a reference cue by which the dancing bee normally orients herself. Hence, for example, 30° to the right of the light source means 30° to the right of the sun. Another experimental trick the young investigator took advantage of was based on the knowledge of the function of the three simple eyes, called ocelli, on the top of the bee's head. When the ocelli are blacked out, a bee's threshold sensitivity to light is six times higher. Consequently, she requires a much stronger light on the comb to redirect her dances.

The student got a fantastic idea, which he at once tested. If it would work, it would enable him to set up a crucial test of the language hypothesis! He had ocelli-blackened bees perform dances on a comb with a dim light source. With satisfaction he observed that the dancers themselves did not respond to this light. However, the other bees with normal ocelli, who followed the dances, treated the light as if it were the sun. Consequently, they should be misled on direction and sent to a wrong place.

The decisive experiment was set up. The ocelli-blackened dancers were kept foraging at one dish of a fanned array of dishes placed 400 metres from the hive. All recruits were anaesthetized as they arrived at the dishes. Every 30 minutes the light on the comb was moved so the angle apparently being indicated was also moved. The new recruits were shifted by an equivalent angle across the array of dishes on a circle of 400 m radius. They were sent to the dishes which none of the half-blinded foragers had ever visited. Therefore, no scents could have been brought back to the hive from these falsely reported stations. This result completely refuted the olfaction hypothesis and vindicated von Frisch's original ideas.

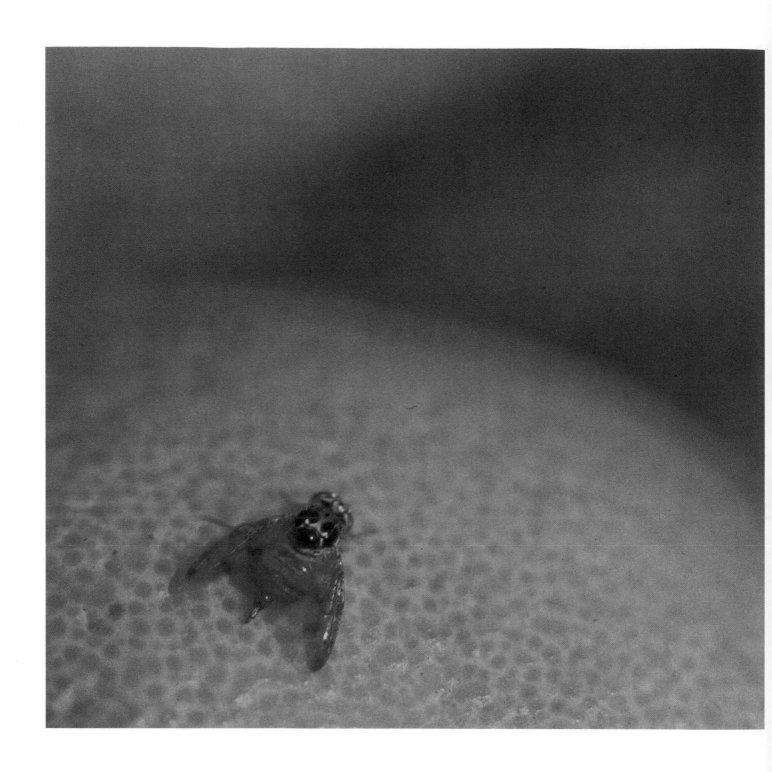

In an untended cherry orchard, one may find a little white 'worm' in nine out of ten cherries during a wormy year. It is the maggot of the cherry fruit fly (*Rhagoletis cerasi*). Hardly a cherry can be found, however, hosting more than one larva. It looks as if the females made an agreement among themselves to lay only one egg in each fruit. However unbelievable it may seem, such an agreement does exist. A female, on depositing her egg in a cherry, leaves on the fruit surface something we suppose to be a chemical message of 'occupied, try again elsewhere' to ensure that another female will not lay an egg in the same fruit. The compound that the fly used for marking the cherry is called a marking pheromone.

A CALLING CARD ON THE CHERRY TREE

Marking pheromones

Females of the Mediterranean fruit fly (*Ceratitis capitata*) deposit their eggs under the skin of citrus fruits.

Such a scented calling card is produced during an elaborate ceremony of oviposition. With a bit of patience, we can observe this for ourselves. An ovipositing cherry fruit fly is by no means shy. On landing on the cherry, the female tours the fruit surface, occasionally touching it with her extended proboscis. If the fruit is still unclaimed territory, the inspection takes about half a minute. If the fruit is already occupied by an egg, the female will leave it in a few scant seconds. As soon as she is certain that her chosen fruit carries no mark, the female drills a hole into it with her ovipositor and lays an egg beneath the fruit's skin. She then immediately walks rapidly around the cherry, dragging her extended ovipositor behind her. After completing each circle, she stops for a moment, changing direction a little. With these motions she is releasing her marking pheromone.

If we continue our watch of a marked cherry, we may witness the magic power of the pheromone. The next female quickly learns, after a few steps, that the fruit is inhabited and leaves to search another fruit. Cherry fruit flies have their gustatory sense organs on the bottom of their forelegs (tarsi) and are able to detect the scent merely by stepping on it. This was ingeniously demonstrated by Dr. Ronald J. Prokopy, who first discovered the pheromone. After having dipped the forelegs of gravid females into melted paraffin, he observed that the would-be mothers carelessly laid their eggs in fruits already taken. The paraffin slippers prevented the females from 'tasting' the surface of the fruit. If we hinder the female from marking the cherry after she deposited her egg by, for instance, scaring her away, another female may come later to add her egg to the same fruit. Should she also be prematurely driven away, a third female might contribute her own egg. The little cherry will become pretty crowded after all the eggs hatch. The strongest larva usually solves the situation with radical action: it attacks and eats its fruitmates. Apparently the mothers have good reason for respecting the chemical messages of other females for the benefit of their own offspring. The local population of cherry fruit flies is in turn guaranteed that as many cherries as possible are utilized.

Marking pheromones are also in the repertoire of many other insects. Some hymenopterous parasitoids use them to facilitate the search for their hosts: the larvae or pupae of other insects. When a female is searching, she leaves marks

The female of the largest European ichneumonid wasp, *Rhyssa persuasoria,* bores into wood with her ovipositor to deposit the eggs in large larvae of wood-destroying insects.

behind wherever she goes. Her message reads: 'Searching here is in vain! I've been here already.' Every other female that visits the place later will receive this message and waste no time before flying off to search elsewhere.

A similar information system has developed among canines. It was observed that foxes or wolves mark their useless food leftovers, such as gnawed bones or bird wings, with their urine. They likewise mark entrances to the empty burrows of their prey, rabbits, red squirrels, minks or similar small rodents. The aim of this behaviour is to increase the efficiency of the search for food. The animal wastes no time investigating remnants when they are marked as inedible. In wolves, this is not surprising, they are social animals and members of a pack help one another. The fox, however, is a solitary hunter. Yet this social adaptation has developed in its species also.

Let us return to our study of insects for a while. Some species use special oviposition pheromones to mark and to call others to suitable places for laying eggs. For instance, gravid female mosquitoes are informed about the suitability of a particular water reservoir by compounds given off by the offspring of other females, which are already successfully developing in the water. The advantage of such a larval lure is that new gravid mosquitoes can lean on the success of previous female's experience. They can thereby avoid the necessity of trying new, untested waters, which may dry out before the mosquito larvae complete their development.

It may happen, however, that the puddle attracts the attention of too many mosquito females at once, and the number of larvae will tax the available food supply drastically. In this case, the older larvae begin to release another pheromone which slows down the development of younger larvae. Only when the older puddle dwellers leave the water can the suppressed younger ones resume their further development. In favourable conditions, however, the mosquito larvae fare much better if more of them live together. Indeed, when the same number of mosquito eggs were divided into two jars, one containing water in which a previous generation of larvae had undergone development, the other with clean water (both batches being equally fed), the larvae of the former batch grew faster and became adults sooner. Why? Because their predecessors left them a chemical message of 'bon appetite', which scientists call the autophagostimulatory pheromone.

An extraordinary marking pheromone has recently been discovered in leaf-cutting ants (Attini), which are often fearful pests on plantations in the tropics of the New World. The ants feed exclusively on a special fungus which they grow in their underground gardens. The fungus has never been found outside of the ants' nest. It is no wonder that a young queen carries the fungus spores in special pouches under her mouth parts as a precious wedding present, to start her own garden in a new nest. The leaf-cutters grow the fungi on a special substrate produced by chewing small bits of leaves or blossoms, other plant materials and caterpillar droppings. In addition, they fertilize the fungus beds with their own faeces.

The material for the substrate is collected from the broad surroundings of the nest by well-organized teams. Some ants cut the plants, others carry the pieces to the nest, still others convert it into the fertile substrate. It is notable that the cutters mark each piece of leaf with a chemical that serves as a scented dispatch document for the guards at the entrance, who inspect each load. Without it, nothing is allowed into the nest. It is a security measure which ensures that nothing harmful will be brought home.

Some bark beetles are known to perform well-organized attacks on the host tree. The first beetles to emerge usually select a suitable tree. By means of an aggregation pheromone, they attract the other members of the local population,

The author of this piece of graphic art is the spruce bark beetle (*Ips typographus*). The main vertical galleries under the bark are bored by a female, whereas side tunnels are made by the larvae that emerge from the

174

and together they make a mass attack which will kill the chosen tree. Only such an organized, sudden and swift onslaught has any chance of success. Healthy trees defend themselves against individual beetles with a discharge of thin resin.

Many scientists have devoted their professional careers to the study of bark beetles. One was an American professor of Slovak origin, Dr. J. A. Rudinski, who worked at Oregon State University. His conclusions concerning the communication of the Douglas fir beetle (*Dendroctonus pseudotsugae*) sound virtually unbelievable. In this species, the scout beetles are females. On the selected tree, their first action is to divide the available space in order to ensure that their galleries under the bark will not cross. Apparently the females communicate by stridulation; each of them gives off a faint sound and tries to keep out of the hearing range of her neighbours. Simultaneously they release an aggregation pheromone which attracts more females to the tree. When enough beetles have accumulated, they attack the tree in unison. Each female will bore a nuptial chamber. Another aggregation pheromone released from the frass (a sawdust-like faeces left behind by a boring female) will attract the males. Before entering the nuptial chamber, the male asks for permission by a short stridulation sound. The female answers, also with a sound. As soon as the male hears her assent, he begins to release a masking (or anti-aggregation) pheromone which cancels the effects of the female aggregation pheromone. At this time the female also stops releasing her attractant and, upon hearing the male's voice, begins releasing her own masking scent. Now, from the chamber of the newly-weds, a chemical message announces: 'Occupied. Private. No trespassing!' All latecomers must then colonize neighbouring trees. As a result, groups of dead trees stand amidst healthy ones, typifying the damage done by these forest pests.

Bark beetles of the genus *Ips* are polygamous. The nuptial chamber is always made by the male. Several females, attracted by his pheromone, regularly share it with him. The number of wives depends on the species but is usually fixed and strictly observed within the individual species. For instance, in *Ips confusus,* there are regularly three females, and in the case of the pine bark beetle (*Ips pini*), there are four. The female is obliged to ask for permission to enter the chamber by a short stridulation. If the male already has his quorum of mates, he will not let other females in, no matter how urgently they call. It is still a mystery how the male knows that his harem is full.

The pheromones of the bark beetles have been thoroughly studied by scientists all over the world for a strongly practical reason. Their synthetic versions are believed to be one of the means of control of these serious forest pests in the future. As a matter of fact, in several European countries, a synthetic bait for the spruce bark beetles (*Ips typographus*) is already commercially available. Hundreds of thousands of special traps using this bait are set every year in endangered areas to suppress local populations of the bark beetles. A single trap may catch tens of thousands of beetles in a season. With the right timing and proper use, this new method may help regulate the beetles' population densities and significantly prevent their devastating outbreaks.

eggs the female has left behind along the main gallery. Note that the tunnels never cross, which may serve as circumstantial evidence that the beetles and their larvae communicate somehow with each other.

The bolas spider of the genus *Mastophora* attracts the males of certain moth species by an imitation of the sex pheromone of their own females. The bolas makes no webs to catch the prey. Instead, the spider casts a sticky ball dangling at the end of a silk line, toward the flying prey.

IT PAYS TO KNOW THE LANGUAGE OF YOUR ENEMY

Chemical communication between species

The bolas is a huntig weapon used by South American Indians. It consists of one or more balls, connected by short strings to both ends of a long rope. The bolas is skilfully thrown at targets.

In the summer of 1977, great numbers of large, peculiar spiders appeared on a barbed wire fence near the campus town of Melandes, Colombia. Although they were related to the web spiders, they did not spin the usual circular web to catch prey. Yet they did not suffer any shortage of food. An arachnologist, Dr. William Eberhard, noticed them and decided to investigate their mysterious way of hunting. The subject of his interest was a rare spider of the genus *Mastophora,* locally known as the bolas. The hunting technique of the bolas is quite unique. The spider spins a single horizontal line instead of a whole web. Hanging suspended from the middle of this line is another line with a small sticky ball at its end, as a pendant. A hunting spider hangs on the horizontal line by all four of the legs on one side of its body, while holding the string with the ball by the free foreleg of the other side. When a flying insect approaches, the hunter swings the ball at the prey, bolas-style. Should the spider hit the target, the insect gets stuck in the ball. Then the spider drops down to the victim, gives it a venomous bite to immobilize it and starts to feed on it. This much has been known about the behaviour of bolas since the beginning of this century, when they got their common name.

This hunting technique would seem to be extremely inefficient, considering the low probability of a prey insect passing within reach of the spider's weapon, and the even lower probability of the insect being hit by the ball. How can it be that the spider's hunting is such a flourishing business despite all this? Dr. Eberhard had to witness over a hundred of the spiders' hunting successes during numerous moonlit nights before he could answer this question. He finally came to the conclusion that the spiders chemically attract their prey.

A potential victim always approaches the spider in a slow upwind flight with its antennae stretched forward. Should it miss the spider on its first attempt, it doubles back to repeat the manoeuvre. The insect responds to the olfactory lure of the spider from a distance of as much as 10 metres. The spider is alerted to the approaching prey through its sense of hearing; if stimulated by an artificial buzzing tone, it responded as if flying moths were advancing — by a swift swing of the ball. When I tell you that the 165 deceived six-leggers were all males belonging to only one or two species of noctuid moths, you may form the same suspicion as Dr. Eberhard did: To the male moths, the spider apparently smells much like their females do.

Because of the obsession of the male moths for the attractive smell of the sex pheromones of their mates, the bolas spiders' unusual hunting technique is just as effective as the classical one of catching prey in webs. Dr. Eberhard found that the bolas managed to lure an average of one moth every 10 minutes. Although not all the moths came within reach of the sticky ball, and many who did were missed by the spider, yet the mean catch was not bad — 2.2 moths a night. Furthermore, the spider was spared the efforts of maintenance and repair of the web.

We can find many examples of the abuse of chemical language among animals. Members of one species often break the communication code of another species, with benefit to only one of them. The bolas hunting technique is a typical, although unusual example of the use of chemical signals benefiting the one emitting them. The interspecific communication chemicals of this kind are called allomones. We have talked about allomones of a similar type in connection with the delusive blossoms of some orchids. However, the most commonly found allomones belong to defensive secretions.

The scents or fragrances of other species are far more often taken advantage of by the receiving individual. Communication compounds of this kind are called kairomones. If, for instance, a fox uses its sense of smell to hunt down a rabbit, then the latter's scent is a kairomone.

The tiny parasitic wasp *Nasonia vitripennis* finds its host, a fly pupa, by smell.

Such examples are particularly abundant among insects. Searching for prey without the aid of kairomones is rather exceptional within the group. We are all painfully aware that our own bodies are a rich source of attractive compounds for many of those bloodthirsty little creatures.

Almost all hymenopterous parasites can find their host by their sense of smell. The victim's scent traces may be left behind in the salivary secretions that remain in the plant tissue on which the insect feeds, in its faeces or in the silky cocoons. By chance, the wing scales of a female moth may flake off while she is laying her eggs, leaving a scent which attracts egg parasites.

Some nestmates of the ants or termites take advantage of understanding the language of their hosts with a cunning unparalleled in the insect kingdom. It is surprising to note that 'intelligent' ants, who seldom tolerate the presence of visitors of their own species from different colonies, are fooled by 'dumb' beetles, mites, millipedes, springtails, silverfish, crickets, cockroaches, bugs, lacewings, caterpillars or flies. Ants not only tolerate them, but even give deference to them at the expense of their own health. As the famous American myrmecologist, W. M. Wheeler, put it: 'Were we to behave in an analogous manner we should live in a truly Alice in Wonderland society. We should delight in keeping porcupines, alligators, lobsters etc. in our homes, insist on their sitting down to table with us and feed them so solicitously with spoon victuals that our children would either perish of neglect or grow up as hopeless rhachitics.'

Behind the success of these slothful spongers is, once again, nothing other than breaking their hosts' communication codes. Such nestmates of ants (myrmecophiles) or termites (termitophiles) use their adeptness at language to get everything they need.

First, the myrmecophiles must find the ants. That is why they have learned, during a long evolution, to understand the ants' trail pheromones. The next prerequisite for settling into the good life is mastering the art of intruding into the colony and being accepted there. A commonly used tactic is based on first attracting a worker ant and then offering her an 'appeasement' compound, which will lessen her wariness and aggressiveness. For this purpose, myrmecophilous or termitophilous species have developed various ectodermal glands, giving secretions that are very attractive to the worker and soldier ants. An example for this is

Secretions from the abdominal glands of the rove beetle *Atemeles pubicolis* must be a special delicacy for the ants. The ants not only tolerate the beetle among themselves but even feed it.

178

Atemeles pubicolis is in the habit of seasonally changing its hosts. In the autumn, young beetles leave the nest of Formica ants and move into the nest of Myrmica ants. In the spring, they return to their original hosts, where they reproduce. Because of maintaining separate summer and winter quarters, the rove beetles must master two foreign languages. The reason for all these periegrinations is a gastronomic one: the Formica ants do not feed and maintain their larvae over winter, while the Myrmica ants do.

the formula for action which the rove beetle *Atemeles pubicolis* uses when it seeks adoption. It circles the ant nest, looking for an encounter with a worker ant. The ant who accosts the beetle is far from friendly. To avoid attack, the beetle offers an appeasement compound from the tip of its abdomen. As the ant enjoys this offering, its aggressiveness fades away. As a follow-up, the rove beetle 'slips a mickey' to the ant. It foists upon the hapless drinker a second potion from another specialized gland, called an adoption compound. After tasting this delicacy, the ant gently takes the beetle into its mandibles and carries it to the nest as a fond pet. There the intruder absorbs the colony odour and the ants treat it as if it were one of them, grooming and feeding it as they do other members of the colony.

The beetle and its offspring can live happily ever after in the ant-hill. The beetle larvae also fool their hosts by perfuming themselves with a compound that has effects similar to those of the ant brood pheromone – a chemical by which the nurse ants identify their own larvae. Mistaking the beetle larvae for their own brood, the ants take great care of the intruder's young, offering them rich liquefied food from their crops and nursing them in the brood chambers together with their own offspring. This particularly suits the predatory intentions of the rove beetles; they consume their roommates without inhibition.

There is one large group of 'ant associates' from whom the ants benefit. These are the aphids, the soft-bodied little insects that suck plant sap. The main nutrients from the plant which aphids utilize are those containing nitrogen, such as proteins. Sugars are excreted from their anus as waste together with excess water, forming the so-called honeydew. Many ant species have learned to collect this sweet delicacy. They lick it not only from the leaf surface, but directly from the tip of the aphids' abdomens. Some ants can even 'milk' the aphids. They stimulate the region around the aphid's anus with their antennae for as long as the aphid releases droplets of the nectar.

Some ants are in the habit of building special 'stalls' of clay or mud for their 'cattle' – aphid species – which feed on the underground parts of plants. These small chambers are closely guarded. The American ants of the genera *Acanthomyops* and *Acropyga* are supposed to live exclusively on the products of their underground herds. They obtain the necessary proteins to supplement their diet by slaughtering some of their 'cows'. Thus it can be said that these ants keep aphids for 'milk and meat'. For this reason, the ants meticulously care for the winter eggs of the aphids. If the ant nest is disturbed, they carry the eggs to a place of safety with the same attentiveness they give to their own brood.

In return for the sweet honeydew the aphids give, the ants provide complete protection. If an unguarded aphid is attacked by a predator, it warns all the other aphids on the leaf with an alarm pheromone, to which they respond by dispersing or dropping to the ground. However, aphids guarded by ants disperse much less readily, if at all. Sometimes they only excitedly shiver, relying apparently on their protectors more than on their own defence system. When an ant smells the aphid alarm pheromone, it unfailingly comes to the rescue. Ants will pounce on any ladybug that wants to feed on their herd, forcing the beetle to leave the scene. If we simulate an attack by harassing an aphid with forceps, the afflicted aphid will release its smelly call. The ants will respond by gathering to defend the endangered individual. With their mandibles open threateningly, they may even attack the forceps. The same vigour would be used to show aggression toward a piece of filter paper soaked in farnesene, a synthetic aphid alarm pheromone.

Despite all the protection offered by the ants, aphids can easily become victims of a devious parasitoid. A little braconid wasp, *Paralipsis enervis,* is well adapted for underground life. The ants not only put up with its presence in their nest, but even feed the adult wasps and partially nibble off their wings to discourage them from leaving. And how do the wasps repay their hosts for such foster-care? They lay eggs on their 'cattle'. The larvae from these eggs hatch out and eat the ants' prized aphids.

Plainly there is a lot of exploitation going on in Nature. It is not rare for one species of ant to exploit another ant species. Once again, the victorious advantage goes to those who master the chemical language of the others. Physical strength counts for nothing in such an uneven relationship.

About forty years ago, an obscure ant was discovered in the isolated valley of Saas Fe in the Swiss Alps. It was given the name *Teleutomyrmex schneideri*. These ants live as social parasites with a common European ant species, *Tetramorium caespitum*. They rely on their hosts so much that the parasitic female no longer produces worker ant eggs of her own. She spends most of her life riding on the back of her host-queen and lets the host worker ants feed her, or she steals food directly from the mouth of her host while the latter is being fed. The parasitic female lays her eggs among the eggs of her carrier, and the host worker ants will care for them as if they were their own. For some, still unknown reasons, the parasitic queen causes the host queen to lay only worker eggs.

There is only one explanation for the way *Tetramorium* ants tolerate their tyranical royal visitor: the *Teleutomyrmex* ant has learned the communication code of its involuntary hosts. The parasitic female has little glands all over her body which produce a substance that must be an attractive delicacy for the host worker ants. Elated by the taste of this substance, they are not only willing to tolerate the foreign queen but also to serve her until they drop. Ultimately, such behaviour destroys their colony. The queen probably wins their favour at the very first encounter, for she has little problem in entering the host nest. It is worth noting that these parasitic ants are understood only on the eastern slopes of the Saas Fe valley. Elsewhere, they would be rejected by the host species. Why should not ants also have their own dialects in the isolated valleys of the Swiss Alps, as do the people?

The queen of another parasitic ant, *Epimyrma stumperi,* is well known for her equally successful method of gaining access to the nest of her host species, *Leptothorax tuberum*. She sneaks as close to the nest entrance as possible. When the first worker ant spots her, she plays dead until the worker calms down. Then she climbs up onto the worker's back and gathers the colony smell from her carrier with special brushes on her forelegs, smearing the scent all over her own body. Smelling like the members of the host colony, she is easily accepted by them.

The conquering of a related ant species takes a completely different approach when practised by the slaver ants. At first glance, their methods may superficially resemble those of humans.

Slaver ants provide themselves with a working force by making raids on colonies of related species. Their expeditions are dramatic events, during which troops of slaver ants march toward the nests of potential slave ants, breaking into them and pillaging the nests of their pupae, which are brought back to the slavers' nest. There, worker ants will emerge from the pupae and become an integral part of the slaver ant nest. Workers of the evolutionarily most advanced slaver ant species are capable only of fighting and pillaging. Hence, all the other communal chores, such as foraging for food, constructing and repairing the nest or caring for the brood of the slavers, falls on the shoulders of the slaves.

Particularly in pop-science literature, there exists a wealth of drastic descriptions of the violence and destruction created by closely organized lines of the six-legged slavers, who leave in their wake battlefields strewn with the torn bodies of their victims. While I do not want to deny entirely such horrifying stories, they are often

The brood pheromones, compounds produced by immature individuals of ants, attract the worker ants and induce brood care behaviour in them.

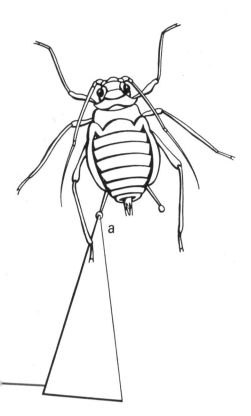

By now, at least 35 species of slaver ants have been described. They occur only in the temperate zone.

An attacked aphid releases the alarm pheromone, which makes the other aphids on the leaf disperse. The active compound of the pheromone comes from a pair of horny outlets of the glands (a) located on the tip of the abdomen. Alarm among aphids can also be experimentally induced by placing among them a piece of filter paper soaked in this compound.

exaggerated and full of subjective bias. We would do better to concentrate on another and rather neglected aspect of dulosis (a more appropriate term for slavery in ants): the problems of communication among slaver ant soldiers, and communication of the slavers with their slaves in everyday life.

All observations of slavers' raids agree on one point: the phalanx progresses quickly and unwaveringly toward the victims' nest. How do ants know which direction to take, and from where does their certainty come? The mystery was solved by a Harvard professor, Edward O. Wilson, at least twenty years ago. The slaver ant's scout, on discovering a nest to be plundered, returns in a straight line to the home colony to announce the news to her nestmates. On her way home, she leaves behind chemical marks made by the trail pheromone. In the home nest, she will alarm and recruit the soldiers — by smell. Following her trail, the army will rush unerringly toward the target.

Professor Wilson was able to stage a small slavers' expedition in his laboratory. In the afternoon, when ants normally leave for their raids, he painted bogus trails with an extract derived from warriors' bodies, which led away from the entrance of their artificial nest. The slaver ants responded as they do at the beginning of each expedition: they left the nest and excitedly followed the invisible painted trail. When the professor put a colony of their regular slave species in the trail, a fight broke out. The slavers brought the pupae of the attacked ants back to their nest.

The battlefield success of the slaver ants can be attributed not only to their fighting skills, strength or sharpness of their mandibles, but also the power of their chemical weapons. The robber-ants have developed greatly enlarged glands for producing the alarm pheromones. They use these pheromones as war propaganda, as a scented 'call to arms' to intimidate and 'demoralize' their quarry. An excess of the pheromones 'deafens' the chemical communication of the defenders, preventing them from organizing effective defence action. This enables the slaver ants to abduct the pupae of the surprised victims, sometimes completely unopposed.

Considering the ants' well known intolerance toward strangers, we must surely be surprised by the fact that slavers and slaves can get along together in a common nest. This may be partially due to the close relatedness of the ant species in question, which in turn accounts for similarities in their colony odours. In addition, young slave ants become adapted to the slavers' odour during the first few hours after emergence from the pupae. Later, however, they become intolerant of strange odours. That is why slaves usually do not tolerate the presence of abducted pupae, if other than their own species, except as fodder for a meal. It is common, therefore, for there to be slaves of only one species in any one nest despite the fact that slavers occasionally rob from several different species in their neighbourhood.

Ants often protect aphids from their predators. The ants are rewarded by droplets of the sweet liquid which the aphids excrete from their anus whenever stimulated by a touch from the ant's antennae.

AVOIDING PREDATION

Sooner or later, the occasion arises when an animal needs to communicate with its enemy. Because its life is often at stake, the message should be emphatic and clearly understandable. In most cases, it certainly is. Even man can often understand it without the aid of a dictionary. He is, after all, frequently one of the most dangerous enemies of many animals. This is particularly so when the animal has no other predators because of its size, strength or isolated occurrence. Prey species use a variety of tactics to make it more difficult for predators to provide themselves with food. They increase their chances by leading a secretive life, by camouflaging themselves, by using threatening or intimidating gestures or postures (especially if they possess some good weapon as a bargaining device), by pretending to be someone else, or by using a wealth of other artifices. A host of animals find it advantageous to rely on each other's warning signals when danger appears. The solidarity among threatened individuals may culminate in a unity of effort against a common enemy and wreck its predatory intentions. All these actions call for a common language. The catalogue of techniques and tricks developed to surmount or outwit the enemy is voluminous. A few samples from this lexical arsenal will conclude our excursion through the realms of animal language.

The north African gecko *Tarentola delalandii* likes to rest on the bark of old trees, where it is well camouflaged.

Merely by its appearance, an animal can befuddle its predators so that they either ignore it or are unable to find it at all. The individual in potential trouble can communicate messages which could be expressed, in human language, by several different sentences.

'I am not here!' This tactic zoologists call crypsis. We are all familiar with this 'hide-and-seek' game by animals. It is their common strategy when the odds are against them. In the simplest case, the colour, structures and patterns on the surface of the animal resemble its surroundings. For the camouflage to be perfect, the behaviour of the animal must also be adjusted; the animal has to select the right background, assume the right position and remain there absolutely still. Many moths make it through the day by sitting motionless on tree bark. Some animals can even change their colouration, thus readily adapting themselves to their background. True masters of this technique are squids and octopuses. Of course, the most talented of all is that proverbial lizard, the chameleon. The ability to change colour is not uncommon among lower animals. Many species of crustaceans and fish can also do this. Even caterpillars frequently adopt the colour of the leaves on which they feed.

Thanks to perfect camouflage, some species of duck or pheasant can successfully nest in open, unsheltered places. However, only females show protective colouration, because only they care for the nest. Of course, in those bird species in which the males are also expected to sit on the nest, such as the marsh-wrens or skylarks, both sexes are equally inconspicuously coloured. Problems of this kind do

TACTICS FOR SURVIVAL

Passive defences

184

When a lappet moth (*Gastropacha querci-folia*) is at rest, it closes its wings so that it completely resembles a dry twisted leaf.

The inchworm's defence lies in pretending to be a dry twig.

not trouble birds that nest in tree hollows or similar cavities: both parents can look alike and be quite colourful. This is the case for titmice, nuthatches and woodpeckers, to name a few.

The snowy white dress of arctic birds and mammals protects them well all winter long, but for the short summer they must change their attire. Such a seasonal change of colour occurs in the snowshoe hare (*Lepus americanus*) and in the rock ptarmigan (*Lagopus mutus*).

Insects are unbeatable in mimicking inanimate, unpalatable or disgusting objects. Does not the lappet moth in the picture above look like a dead dry leaf? Another example of this kind can be found on the bottom of every pond and stream. Larvae of the caddis flies form silken cases for their soft bodies and harden and camouflage them with various materials from the surroundings. Other species use sand, needles of various conifers, or other fragments of vegetation. Some inchworms perfectly imitate a twig on a tree (left). Caterpillars of some butterflies or moths can even pretend to be bird droppings, being meticulous in such details as having white at one end. Some garden spiders are in the habit of waiting for prey in the middle of their webs. In order to distract attention from its vulnerable body, the spider weaves silk dummies of itself, incorporating remnants of former prey, which it places nearby on the web. It is speculated that these surrogates may save the spider's life, eventually.

Other animals have tactics just the opposite to that of protective colouration. They make every effort to be as striking and conspicuous as possible. Their

185

flagrant, gaudy colouration — often a combination of yellow, orange or red with black — together with threatening postures and intimidating noises, are intended to warn each would-be predator. Some small creatures consider even this insufficient, so they form dense aggregations, increasing their impact. Their warning 'beware, we are dangerous' is thus voiced as emphatically as possible. Rather than attempting to hide, they literally flaunt themselves in the face of predators. Why? Simply, if one is poisonous, noxious tasting or otherwise nasty or dangerous, then it pays to advertize in order to distinguish oneself from less conspicuous but more palatable prey. Should the predator, by chance, not take the warning seriously, such an unpleasant experience will be long remembered if connected with warning colouration. Next time he will not touch that colourful morsel. Many unrelated dangerous species have similar warning patterns, which is mutually beneficial. One unpleasant lesson will teach the predator to avoid all of them. Examples of warning colouration can often be found among animals who use their striking appearance to advertize their venomous weapons. These include wasps, spiders, poisonous fish or snakes. Others, like caterpillars, beetles or true bugs, proclaim their foul and loathsome taste. Caused by toxic compounds contained in their blood, these distasteful agents induce vomiting or other symptoms of acute poisoning in the predator. This kind of chemical defence is rather costly in terms of the energy required to produce such complex compounds. It is no wonder that some animals 'borrow' deterrent chemicals from their host plants for use in their own defence. The caterpillars of the monarch butterflies (Danaidae), for instance, obtain cardiac

The striking colouration of a Cuban orb-weaver spider of the genus *Gasteracantha* discourages predators from attack.

The conspicuously coloured caterpillar of the spurge hawk-moth (*Celerio euphorbiae*) hardly looks like a tasty titbit.

The linden bug (*Pyrrhocoris apterus*) emphasizes its warning colouration by making large dense aggregations.

glycosides from the milkweed, on which they feed. These glycosides, which induce vomiting in birds, accumulate during the youthful days of the larva and remain in the body of the insect through its adult stage. The monarch boldly announces this chemical defence system by its splashy appearance.

Most animals, however, synthesize their own defence chemicals and 'serve' them to enemies in many different ways. A common means of bestowing retribution is by the stinging hairs — fragile, hollow bristles supplied with tiny venom glands at their bases. Fragments of these hairs easily penetrate the predator's mucous membranes and cause distressing local irritation. Thanks to their hairiness, barbed caterpillars are ignored by most insect-eating birds. Large hairy mygalomorph spiders (Theraphosidae) also may be armed by urticating hairs on their backs, easily shed or rubbed off by the legs, which protect them from small insectivorous mammals.

When noxious arthropods are irritated in some way, they excrete droplets of yellow or orange haemolymph from their leg joints, wings or other parts of the body. Even just the appearance of the coloured liquid signals its venomous nature. Such reflex bleeding is a habit among ladybugs, blister beetles, many other beetles, some butterflies, and also in millipedes. Quite often insects release these repulsive fluids from the mouth or the anus. It is customary for grasshoppers and katydids to use this type of defence. Their toxic secretions serve them well in repelling ants as well as mammals.

Many animals act on the premise 'the best defence is a good offence', using their virulent secretions as a spray gun against the enemy. The chemical warfare of some

The white satin moth (*Leucoma salicis*) releases, when disturbed, droplets of yellow blood which justifiably look poisonous.

ants, for instance, is composed of 50 per cent formic acid. As the soldiers of some species can produce this dangerous compound in amounts of up to one fifth of their body weight, these six-legged warriors must be fearful fighters. The whip-scorpion also packs an even more formidable mixture in a gland at the end of its abdomen, a blend of 84 per cent acetic acid and 5 per cent caprylic acid. The latter compound enhances the caustic effects of the former and aids in its penetration through the skin of an enemy.

When speaking of chemical combatants, the bombardier beetles reign supreme. They shoot hot secretions from the tip of their abdomen at their pursuers. The compound is hot enough to burn the skin of an inexperienced collector. It is generated in a special combustion chamber, in which hydrogen peroxide reacts with hydroquinone in the presence of catalytic enzymes, creating a gaseous mixture heated to 100 °C. It is only the heat-resistant lining of this chamber which protects the bombardier beetle from its own weapon.

Dangerous species usually do not use their weapons without fair warning. As we have seen, they tip the enemy off by body colouration, postures and sometimes by

The threatening, wide open mandibles of the wood ant (*Formica rufa*) do not allow for any hesitation about the seriousness of its determination to attack.

Another original chemical weapon is known in termites of the genus *Nasutitermes*. Their forehead protrudes into a rather long 'nozzle', from which the soldiers shoot an irritating and sticky spray. This adheres to the victim so well that it is unlikely to get rid of it. The weapon is so effective that soldiers no longer need their mandibles for defence; they have become vestigial or have disappeared altogether.

their voice or smell. However, some harmless and palatable species take advantage of the fearsome reputation of other animals by mimicking their warning signals. The predators that learned to avoid the truly dangerous ones also shun these impostors. Pretending to be someone else is called Batesian mimicry and is quite common in Nature. Such faking is, of course, good for the imitator but bad for the original model; it devalues the warning signals. If the number of harmless mimics surpasses the numbers of the dangerous model, predators find it more difficult to learn that the warning signal means danger. They attack both the model and the mimics more often before learning their lesson than if only the noxious species had been encountered. Wasps, bumblebees and ants are the most emulated by fakes. The black-and-yellow-striped patterns of dreaded yellow jackets and hornets can be found among butterflies, flies and beetles, but also among grasshoppers (right).

The hypothesis of the startle effect of suddenly displayed eye-spots on insect-eating birds was experimentally confirmed by a laboratory test. When the hungry bird was just about to pick up the mealworm larva from the top of the light

The most familiar kind of mimicry is Batesian mimicry (false warning colouration), where a protected (armipotent or bad-tasting) species is imitated by an unprotected one. For example, the colour patterns of hornets, yellow jackets or paper wasps (*Polistes*) (right) are mimicked by various insects from different orders, such as the hornet moths, long-horned beetles, meloid beetles or grasshoppers (bottom, from left to right).

box, the researcher suddenly switched on a light which illuminated alternatively transparencies with various patterns placed on each side of the bait. The bird was frightened the most by the eye-spots, which closely resembled those on the wings of hawk-moths (see the picture on p. 191).

Just one look at the coral snake, the most richly coloured limbless reptile of the New World, leaves one certain that the animal is deadly poisonous. There are, however, several species of coral snakes. Some are, indeed, extremely poisonous. The bite of others is very painful but only moderately venomous and is not necessarily fatal. Finally, there are species with warning colouration quite similar to that of the coral snake, which are not at all venomous. Each one of these snakes is respected by predators, regardless of its actual calibre of danger. However, it is still unknown whether the fear is inherent or whether it is based on a previous unpleasant experience. Rarely would any animal have a second chance after receiving the bite of one of the most virulent coral snakes.

'I am not what you thought' is another method of defence skilfully used by various insects. Caterpillars of some arctiid or sphingid moths assume different bizarre warning postures; mostly they elevate and broaden the front part of their body, transforming it into a mock snake's head with large false eyes. The 'snake' may even pretend an attack on the intruder. The effect of all these and similar tricks on small birds can be explained by the birds' innate fear of their own predators, snakes, owls and large birds of prey. They do not take the unnecessary risk of attacking a strange object, particularly if other food is abundant. The moment of hesitation on the part of the predator may offer the prey a life-giving second to escape.

Some unarmed animals have developed still another defence technique, a tactic based on the startle effect. It is used most often by moths and butterflies. For example, all underwing moths (*Catocala*) are well concealed due to the mottled colouration of their forewings, which perfectly mimic the bark of the tree trunks on which the insect rests during the day. If their disguise is discovered they employ their alternative tactic. They surprise the predator with a flash of bright colour from their hind wings, which have previously been hidden beneath the dull cloak of the forewings.

The disguise of the caterpillar of the oleander hawk-moth (*Daphnis nerii*) is perfect.

Many animals deceive their enemies by pretending to be larger than they are in reality. Toads and monitor lizards puff themselves up to extremes. The cobra expands its neck region and sways from side to side, the ostrich flaps its wings and rocks its whole body, and many mammals make their fur 'stand an end'. Some signals are meant to deflect the attack to less vital parts of the body. Predators prefer to attack the head and orientate themselves by its distinct eyes. Fritillaries, swallowtails and some other butterflies take advantage of the predator's attraction to dark spots and show false 'eyes' at the margin or tail of their wings. The notches left by a bird's beak on the wings of older specimens speak eloquently of the usefulness of such fake targets.

The startle effect of a sudden flash of brightly coloured hind wings may be punctuated by the use of eye-spots, as in the eye-spotted hawk-moth (*Smerinthus ocellata*). The spots resemble an angry glare and have a frightening effect on small birds.

A perching eagle owl (*Bubo bubo*) is mobbed by crows and birds of prey, which then become an easy target for the hunter's gun.

We all know them. The raucous voice of an aroused jay (*Garrulus glandarius*) betrays our presence to everyone in the woods. If you hear trains of excited calls from the blackbirds in your backyard you can be sure that a cat is creeping around somewhere in the bushes. Birds of other species also understand such warnings, and they often join the first caller in a loud chorus. These excited birds follow the beast of prey and mob it from a respectful distance. The betrayed hunter knows that it has no chance here and that it need not waste any time in the area. It can only be dangerous when it is unseen. Thus the prime function of the warning signals is an early disclosure of the enemy.

The mobbing of a bird of prey is another variation on the same theme. Ornithologists sometimes use this innate instinct in songbirds when catching them for ringing. They surround a decoy of an owl with mist-nets and sooner or later the nets are alive with an enraged feathery gang. Regretfully, irresponsible hunters often abuse their knowledge of the aversion hawks and crows have to the eagle owl (*Bubo bubo*). They expose an eagle owl in a clearing and ambush the gathering attackers. The present photograph is a sad document of the slaughter that results from this controversial hunting technique. In this case, the target of the hunter's

BEWARE, DANGER!

Warning signals

192

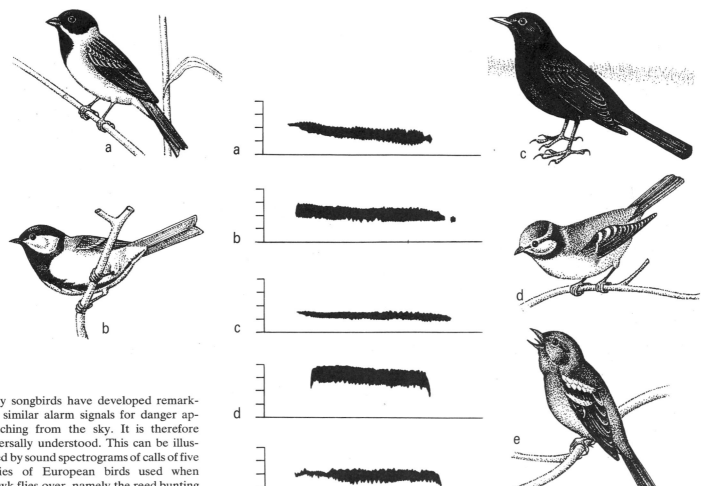

Many songbirds have developed remarkably similar alarm signals for danger approaching from the sky. It is therefore universally understood. This can be illustrated by sound spectrograms of calls of five species of European birds used when a hawk flies over, namely the reed bunting (*Emberiza schoeniclus*) (a), the great tit (*Parus major*) (b), the blackbird (*Turdus merula*) (c), the blue tit (*Parus caeruleus*) (d), and the chaffinch (*Fringilla coelebs*) (e).

gun was a protected bird of prey, the buzzard (*Buteo buteo*). Mobbing is also known in mammals. Troops of baboons or chimpanzees will launch mock attacks accompanied by screeching cries at leopards. Even the California ground squirrels or agoutis will occasionally mob a snake.

In the open terrain of the African savanna, baboons and antelopes nicely complement each other's sensory abilities. The baboons possess excellent sight, while hoofed mammals have an exceptional sense of smell. Their common enemies are the large cats. By co-operating in standing watch, each group is rewarded with an early warning when danger approaches.

There are numerous other examples of a similar multispecific guard duty. In much the same way, the jay in our forest, the peacock (*Pavo cristatus*) in an Indian jungle, or the Egyptian plover (*Pluvialis aegypticus*) in an African swamp warn other inhabitants of their home by loudly announcing the arrival of an intruder. Warning signals are often misinterpreted. Some people think that the animal deliberately announces approaching danger to its neighbours. It is, however, an innate behaviour triggered off by an unfamiliar sound, shape or smell. The animal will emit warning signals even if it has no audience, or if it has been raised in an artificial environment and never met a member of its own or another species.

Warning calls may express more than a general alarm. The call of a songbird will sound different depending on whether it sings warning of a hawk in the air or a cat

on the ground. The bird that first spots a predator on the ground summons others out of harm's way with a 'come here, everyone, look out for the cat' call. Its voice must have acoustic properties such that its fellows can quickly and easily spot it. Only short, sharply defined notes fulfil this need. The voice of some birds resembles a clanging bell when they sound the alarm. If, however, a bird spots a hawk in the air, it broadcasts an aerial warning signal which admonishes 'take cover'. Since the caller itself risks disclosure, the sound must have properties that make it difficult for the predator to localize; it is a low pitched, continuous call which begins and ends gradually.

The repertoire of alarm voices of the vervet monkey (*Cercopithecus aethiops*) consists of four different signals. One is used to warn against the leopard, another against a monkey-eating eagle, still another to warn against a large snake, and the last discloses an approaching baboon or man.

A most sophisticated alarm system has evolved in social rodents. The vocal repertoire of the yellow-bellied marmot (*Marmota flaviventris*), to Westerners better known as the 'rockchuck', contains no less than eight warning signals. An equally rich vocabulary can be found in its relative, the prairie dog (*Cynomys ludovicianus*). These rodents live in huge concentrations called towns that may contain as many as a thousand inhabitants. The town is divided into smaller communities called coteries, each containing some thirty individuals who maintain contact through interconnecting burrows. Several members of each town keep guard on the mounds of excavated soil next to their burrow entrance while the others graze. Should one of them spot an approaching enemy, it releases a series of whistling barks, which specify the kind of danger. The warning call is repeated by the neighbouring guards, spreading the alarm throughout the whole town. The

The black rump of the fallow deer (*Dama dama*) contrasts particularly well with the white rump patch. Movements betray the mood of the animal. If the deer feels safe, it swings its tail contentedly from side to side. A disturbed animal abruptly halts its move-

194

The scorpion *Buthus occitanus* (left) displays its dangerous weapon when threatened.

The desert beetle of the genus *Blaps* (right) does a head stand when endangered. Some ethologists have suggested that by doing so, the beetle mimics the threat posture of its foul-smelling double, the stink beetle (*Eleodes*), with whom it often shares the habitat.

The formic acid that the ant releases into the wound inflicted by its mandibles acts also as an alarm pheromone to summon help.

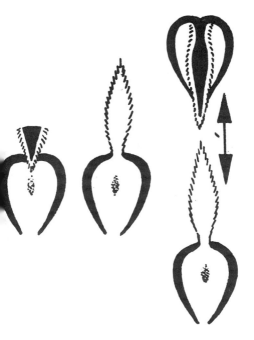

ments and holds its tail still and down. With increasing anxiety, the deer raises its flag up, exposing its white underside. A fully alerted animal flits its tail up and down.

Overleaf: A fallow deer herd.

inhabitants do not take immediate flight into their burrows. Instead, they poise standing on their hind legs in strategic positions in front of their homes, intently watching every move of the approaching intruder. I would not like to be in the shoes of a hungry coyote trotting through such a town, being surrounded by the stares of multitudes of tasty prey that let him come within a tantalizingly short distance and then at the last moment duck into the security of their underground home.

Animals living in groups often warn each other by visual signals. Many use their tail for this purpose. If its underside is pure white, then lifting the tail is all that is needed to give a snappy warning even at dusk. Wild rabbits (*Oryctolagus cuniculus*) are noted for this. Deer and their antlered kin, pronghorns and some other antelopes, have a rump semaphore emphasized by a large patch of white fur, which can be suddenly enlarged by the erection of the hairs when danger is at hand. This flash of white can be seen for a long distance and serves as a signal to other members of the herd to take flight.

Alarm can be announced by smell as well. This was described by Charles Butler way back in 1609. He noticed that honey bees can be provoked into a mass attack by the scent of a compound released from a single sting. Today we know that the sting gland contains not only venom, but also amyl acetate, an alarm pheromone used by the stinging insect to call for help and mark the target.

The alarm is proclaimed in an endangered ant-hill by chemical means too. The worker ants who first encounter the intruder will notify their nestmates and recruit assistance by releasing their alarm pheromones. Anyone can gain first-hand experience with this by a single experiment. If one disturbs a large ant-hill by

195

The prairie dog (*Cynomys ludovicianus*) keeping guard.

tapping on one side of it with a stick, the incited worker ants assume a grotesque posture. With abdomen curved up between the hind legs, each ant ejects a tiny jet of pungent liquid, visible only against the light. The stick that exasperated the ants will then smell of formic acid. This simplest organic acid is a defence secretion as well as an alarm pheromone for many species of ants. These alarm pheromones are used by ants in various situations. They serve to recruit warriors when the colony is setting off on a pillaging expedition, or to call for help when a prey is too large to be handled alone. When a wounded or buried ant needs assistance, it also releases a distress scent composed of alarm pheromones. If an ant detects a scented alarm outside of the nest, it responds by escaping. Within the ant-hill, however, it will bravely rush to give help whenever needed.

The alarm pheromones of the hymenopterans are produced by the glands associated with the mandibles or the sting. The pheromones are thus readily available whenever these weapons are used. Often, the pheromone itself serves as a chemical weapon. It is a great advantage when a single compound can act both as a repellent to the enemy and as a way of alerting the nestmates of danger or calling for their help.

The alarm pheromones are indispensable signals in the chemical vocabulary of all social insects and of many other gregariously living insect species, including aphids, bugs, treehoppers and leafhoppers. Some other animals also rely on them to warn their fellows, such as schooling fish, tadpoles, some water molluscs and perhaps even earthworms. A minnow (*Phoxinus phoxinus*) wounded by a predatory fish will release an alarm substance into the water, to which other fish respond by dispersing. The pheromone comes from the cells of the wounded skin and really packs a wallop: a mere 0.00000005 g (in other words, a five hundred millionth of a gram) of the substance in a cubic centimetre of water is enough to alarm other fish!

■

This particular excursion into the animal kingdom must end here, but the trails we might have taken are endless. One book cannot suffice to mention even briefly all the bits of accumulated knowledge about animal communication which scientists and naturalists have to offer. Rather than pursue such a hopeless task, we have instead had the opportunity to become familiar with the major themes that nearly all animals share when making contact with other creatures. By viewing a few selected entries from Nature's vocabulary, we may send our imaginations to their farthest reaches to contemplate the volume and diversity of messages given and received all around us. Most of the animals' secrets remain inaccessible to humans, but the barrier to understanding our fellow inhabitants of the Earth becomes increasingly less imposing. And this is good, for sooner or later we must find a common language with the creatures with whom we have to co-exist and help to preserve them for future generations. Moreover, by studying the inventions of Nature in the field of communication (which may be millions of years old), engineers often find instruction and inspiration for our own progress in technology. We will let that remain the concern of scientists in the field of bionics. The ambitions of this book will be satisfied if the ordinary reader finds direction for looking and understanding the behaviour of the creatures we encounter throughout life, and if our understanding of the communication that exists beyond the tongue of man brings us pleasure from a more familiar relationship with other cohabitants of our planet.

INDEX

Page numbers in *italic* refer to the illustrations and captions